An Ophthalmologist Looks at Art

ARTHUR LINKSZ, M.D., F.A.C.S.

CONTENTS

Foreword   11

1 Warming Up   15

2 Some Problems in Portraiture   27

3 Self-Portraits   37

4 Right and Left in
     Pictorial Art   73

5 An Ophthalmologist Looks at
     a "Rembrandt" by Rembrandt   95

6 El Greco   103

7 Still More About Painters
     and Astigmatism. A Swedish
     Optician Rekindles the Issue.   117

Summing It All Up   125

Other Books by Dr. Arthur Linksz:

Physiology of the Eye. Volume I. Optics. 1950
Physiology of the Eye. Volume II. Vision. 1952
An Essay on Color Vision and Clinical Color Vision Tests. 1964
On Writing, Reading and Dyslexia. 1973
Visszanezek... (Looking Back: An Autobiography). 1977

PREFACE

This book could only have been written by Dr. Arthur Linksz. It brings together the diverse factors of the science of visual physiology and of the cultural-historical background of art, thus making possible an exhilarating expansion of one's appreciation of art and artists.

Dr. Arthur Linksz is a rare individual. His achievements in the sciences and the arts are eclectic. He is a world-renowned authority in the fields of optics, physiologic optics, color vision and visual physiology. His texts and many papers in these fields stand as testimony to his expertise. Endeavor in any one of these fields would have been sufficient for an ordinary man.

This intellectual giant perceives from his panoramic viewpoint what others could not perceive, synthesize and explain. His unique knowledge of the fundamental sciences and the arts permits him to view related fields with deep insight. For instance, in his book *On Writing, Reading and Dyslexia*, Dr. Linksz presents a completely different viewpoint to those interested in reading problems because of the tremendous knowledge from other disciplines that he brings to bear on the origins, development and conflicts existing in this field.

Sixty years of constantly looking at art through the eye of a vision expert, as well as through the eye of an art historian have culminated in the present book. This book developed from a rich and unusual mixture of background and viewpoint, which was slowly nurtured, incubated, developed and refined to its present form.

I first heard Dr. Linksz present some of the material in this book in a lecture entitled "An Ophthalmologist Looks at Art and Artists." His unique presentation was enthusiastically appreciated by the audience of ophthalmologists. I became determined at that time, many years ago, that the material would reach a wider world of science and art. Dr. Linksz kindly presented the material in a lecture in San Francisco to a mixed audience of scientists and artists under the auspices of The Smith-Kettlewell Eye Research Foundation. The Foundation encouraged Dr. Linksz to record the lectures and copy his slides in order to publish the work presented here. It has been a labor of mutual love.

In the Foreword, Dr. Linksz acknowledges his thanks to his wife, Dr. Julia Linksz, for her aid in helping him collate and organize the final form of the manuscript. And to his older son, Dr. James J. Linksz, for his aid with the illustrations. The Smith-Kettlewell Eye Research Foundation wishes to add its thanks. Additionally, the Foundation wishes to thank Ms. Elizabeth Warner for her constant attention to the project from inception to publication. The Foundation also wishes to thank Miss Isobel Priest, without whose involvement, success would not have been achieved.

The book is pure Arthur Linksz as are all his books. It is highly personal, conversational and completely innovative. There is no fumbling through the minds of others and no clinging to ritualized dogma. Rather, there is a fresh and exhilarating experience which gives both intellectual pleasure in the reading and practical gain in the end. Those who read this book will never again look at art in the same way.

This book has a very special flavor and scope, and could have been written by no one but Dr. Linksz. I express gratitude and thanks to my revered mentor, Dr. Arthur Linksz, for myself and for all who will be fortunate enough to read this monumental contribution to the sciences and the arts.

Arthur Jampolsky, M.D.
for The Smith-Kettlewell
      Eye Research Foundation
San Francisco, California

FOREWORD

Most of my formative years were spent in a small town of about 5,000, mostly farming people, in pre-World War I Hungary. Good soil, little poverty. Catholics were the majority, and the lord of the manor was one of the lesser Esterházys (merely a count — not the prince!).

There was not much chance for exposure to "art" (or whatever one wishes to call it) in a place of this sort. I still remember reproductions of Dürer's "Praying Hands" and of the "Sistine Madonna" in the show window of the local bookstore. A statue, referred to as "Holy Trinity," which stood at the intersection of the main roads was not considered "art." Most people took off their hats and crossed themselves when passing by.

Later on, as a teenager in Bible class, I happened to come across a text with illustrations, some of them by an artist named Rembrandt (I had never heard of him before). At age 14 I took an entrance examination to one of the prestigious collegiate high schools in the country. One of the subjects of the examination was free-hand drawing. I did well, and the examiner took a liking to me. He asked me if I had ever read anything on "art." I had to confess that I had not. So he told me to read "Conversations about Art" by a sculptor named Rodin. This book, the first art book I ever bought, was soon joined by one by the Belgian poet Verhaeren on "Rembrandt." It was not until my university years that I had the opportunity to visit museums. I was fortunate to make some friends who introduced me to the beauties of art and literature and took me along to concerts and the opera.

So that is how it all started — this (by now more than 60 years old) love affair with "art" and books on art. In the beginning it was not a smooth affair. Two world wars and a revolution, followed by a counter-revolution, were hard on both the author and his library. Many of my books were lost or had to be abandoned. Still, I was rather fortunate. I was ultimately able to come to these blessed shores of America and, over the following decades, I could replace many of the books I had lost and add to them others — old and new ones. I also started collecting slides in a rather selective fashion: portraits (especially self-portraits), on the one hand, and, on the other, paintings which documented the artists' awareness and handling of perspective.

As Clinical Professor at New York University and later at New York Medical College, Department of Ophthalmology, I wrote a two volume textbook: *Physiology of the Eye: I Optics and II Vision.* While teaching optics and visual physiology, I was able to use some of those art slides to make my lectures more lively and more interesting. In fact, many of my students recalled years later how my presentations contributed to their becoming ophthalmologists with an "eye" for art. Being myself an ophthalmologist with this kind of eye, I cannot help but look at artworks as an eye doctor as well as a connoisseur. Sometimes I probably notice details which others will not. Quite naturally, I am interested in the pictorial representation of eye diseases and blindness. I also pay special attention to the treatment of the eyes in portraits. I shall try, in this book, to give examples of what an ophthalmologist might see when looking at works of art.

I have, also, for many years been interested in the history of writing, especially its kinetics, in the role of right-handedness in the ultimate evolution of Greco-Latin alphabets, and the problems inevitably met by the left-hander. Some of my best friends are left-handers, and I must thank them for sharing their problems and their insights with me. The end product of my preoccupation with the problems of the poor reader and, in a more general fashion, with writing and reading in various cultures were the subjects of my volume, *On Writing, Reading and Dyslexia,* published in 1973. A chapter of this book is devoted to writing kinetics and I feel that the kinetics involved in the artist's creative activity are, in many ways, comparable — although a much more complex process.

My book *An Essay on Color Vision* published in 1964 dealt with one particular aspect of seeing although, inevitably, it touched on important aspects of what could be called the sensory physiology of color vision — all those more or less hypothetical retinal or neural mechanisms which supposedly culminate in the sensation of color.

A precursor of this volume was a presentation in 1962 at a meeting of the Federation of American-European Medical Societies. It was followed by another presentation on the same topic at a meeting of a New York ophthalmological society. The material grew as I was invited to present it at various professional meetings and courses. The lectures were more or less adapted to a "lay" audience, until in 1968 I was invited to participate as a panel member in a Symposium on Art and Ophthalmology arranged by my friend, Dr. Arthur Jampolsky at the Smith-Kettlewell Institute of Visual Sciences, Pacific Medical Center, San Francisco, California. I was strongly encouraged by my colleagues to organize my seemingly enormous material into the confines of a book. The pictures used in this text are duplicated from my slide collection. Their sole purpose and justification are to document the points raised and discussed in the text. The present edition has been made possible by a grant from the Smith-Kettlewell Eye Research Foundation.

I wish to express my sincere thanks:

To my beloved wife, Dr. Julia Linksz, whose never failing encouragement, knowledgeable assistance and apt criticism helped in organizing and putting in its final form hundreds of pages of the original manuscript.

To my older son, Dr. James J. Linksz, for helping me to locate and acquire books, catalogues and, especially, a sizable collection of slides which enabled me to document my observations.

To my very dear friend, Dr. Arthur Jampolsky, Founding Director of the Smith-Kettlewell Institute of Visual Sciences, for his sponsorship, ongoing patience and generous support which enabled me to realize a project that was on my mind for nearly twenty years.

1 WARMING UP

I will start this presentation by showing one of the supreme master-pieces of all ages, a portrait-bust of Queen Nefertiti (Fig. 1a) which now stands in a Berlin museum. Photographs usually show only a side view of it — the right side. Seeing the original and facing it (as in Fig. 1b), one cannot help experiencing a mild shock — one of her eyes — the left eye — is missing. How did this beautiful woman lose an eye? Did she really have only one eye? Did she perchance have trachoma, the Egyptian eye disease? (This, I remember, was my first thought.) When I visited Egypt nearly forty years ago, trachoma was still ravaging there and blind and one-eyed persons were a common sight. In any event, here we have a work of art — the portrait-bust of a woman, of an individual, of a ravishing beauty — done in those few but glorious years of Pharaoh Ikhn-aton, and one of her eyes is missing. (A modern copy in the Metropolitan Museum of Art in New York City represents her with no eye missing. But that amounts to falsification.)

Next I want to show a photograph of a *huaco*, a pre-Columbian jug

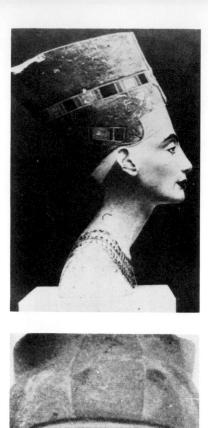

Fig. 1a

Fig. 1b

Fig. 2

Fig. 3

Fig. 4

Fig. 5

from Peru (Fig. 2). It too happens to be in a museum in Berlin. (This photograph comes from the collection of Professor Adalbert Fuchs of Vienna.) It represents the head of a young man with his right eye missing. The other eyeball is either too big or it is protruding. (A tumor behind the eyeball or thyroid malfunction could be causing such a protrusion.) The mouth is asymmetrical, as if the subject also had had Bell's palsy. Here we have, then, several, most likely unrelated kinds of pathology presented in one subject — the missing eye possibly the most prominent among them. Is it, we ask ourselves, the likeness of an individual with all these afflictions? This is unlikely since *huacos* usually do not depict individuals but conditions, sometimes several of them and not necessarily related.

There is quite some distance in space and time between this *huaco* and a sandstone bust in the Museum of the Strasbourg Cathedral (Fig. 3). Still, the same condition is obvious. It also represents a case of Bell's palsy — the mouth is distorted and the left eye widely open — enlarged, bulging, its life gone. My feeling is that this is not just a depicted condition (as it probably is in the *huaco*). It is a person, an individual, suffering. It is a European work of art, late 15th century, and this fact accounts for the difference.

The next picture (Fig. 4) is that of a one-eyed musician — a lovely painting I discovered roaming through the Louvre some years ago. It is attributed to a 16th century artist named Marc Duval. This is all I know about the painting's provenance. What kind of disease or injury could have caused the one-eyedness is hard to guess. Possibly it was the shrinking of an injured eyeball that makes the lids appear to fall back into the sockets. I don't think that enucleation (surgical removal of an eye) was being practiced at the time this portrait was painted. But I don't really know.

Now, I will proceed with a picture of a blind person (Fig. 5). This is a painting (a very early one) by Rembrandt, depicting an episode (an argument about a goat) from the story of Tobit and his wife, Anna. The agony of not being able to see is quite poignantly presented.

The biblical story of Tobit, of his blindness and miraculous cure, must have been a favorite of Rembrandt's. Quite a few of his paintings, drawings and etchings deal with the story — one of the loveliest novellas in the Apocrypha. Tobit becomes blind and his son, Tobias, cures his blindness by applying the gall of a fish to his eyes. The cure is suggested to the son by a strange companion called Azaria, who turns out to be the angel Raphael. In the biblical story, Tobit must have acquired an inflammation of his corneas and this is probably the first indication that some kind of biological had been in use for the treatment of an eye disease some twenty-two centuries ago. Some later paintings of the great Master Rembrandt, as well as several of his drawings and etchings, depict the same scene (Figs. 6 and 7). By the way, Azar-Ya means God Ya — the Helper; Rapha-El means God El — the Healer. Thus the Bible suggests that it is actually God who is the healer using Tobias merely as his intermediary. But even if this is so, we might credit Tobias as having been the first ophthalmologist. And much of our healing — we must confess — is still by the grace of the Lord.

And this brings me to a beautifully appointed little volume by Professor W. Jaeger of Heidelberg, Germany. It deals with artistic, mostly medieval representations of the healing of the blind, especially with the miraculous deeds of Christ as recorded in the Gospels. I want to show at least one of the illustrations — a detail from a late 15th century stained glass window in the Frauenkirche in Munich (Fig. 8).

Those knowledgeable in the Gospels will not be surprised to find different versions of the same event. The story in two of the synoptic Gospels (Mark & Luke) tells about a blind man named Bar-Timeus, whom Jesus reassured it was his faith that cured him. The blind man in the fourth Gospel (John) is being cured by a miracle-working man who applies a mixture of earth and spittle to the blind man's eyes — by a man called Jesus (is he just a man?) whose purported miracles are being watched by a group of disconcerted Pharisees. Most of the illustrations in Jaeger's book deal with the latter and the more dramatic event in which Jesus and his future adversaries rather than the blind man are the principal *dramatis personae.*

Fig. 6

Fig. 7

Fig. 8

Fig. 9

Fig. 10

Fig. 11

A drawing by Rembrandt (Fig. 9, also reproduced in Jaeger's book) and two early El Greco paintings belong in this group. (I shall say more about the El Greco in a later chapter.)

Pictures with realistic details of blind or diseased eyes have rarely any place in a work of art. It is usually the emptiness of gaze that artists try to depict. One of the most moving portrayals of blind people is a painting by Pieter Bruegel, the Elder, in the National Museum of Naples, Italy. I shall return to it once more later (see Fig. 97).

It seems to me that art and clinical ophthalmology have few areas in common. Possibly cross-eyes, wall-eyes (eyes, respectively, converging or diverging more than they should) might be among the few eye conditions which would catch an artist's attention. In his delightful book, *The World through Blunted Sight,* the British ophthalmologist, Patrick Trevor-Roper, presented several examples, one of which I include here. Figure 10 is the portrait of Cardinal Inghirami by Raphael — a case of divergent squint with protrusion and upward turn of a seemingly enlarged right eyeball. The subject of this painting could have been extremely nearsighted in that right eye. (It might be of interest to note that this portrait exists in two identical versions — one in Florence, and the other in the Museum of Fine Arts in Boston. Raphael might have painted both of them.)

Divergent strabismus (wall-eyes) is frequently encountered among El Greco's imaginary portraits of saints. Figure 11, known as St. Bernhard, is one of them. It is a quite realistic portrait of a man with a divergent left eye.

There are two more items to be mentioned in connection with the divergence of eyes, of the lines of gaze — one of these is the celebrated case of divergent squint, the affliction of the great German painter, Albrecht Dürer. (I shall say more about this in further chapters.) The other item is rather insignificant and will be mentioned only briefly. Looking at portraits of elegant ladies by fashionable painters (usually they are commissioned portraits), we notice that the eyes are often drawn somewhat diverging. This is supposed to give a pleasant and dreamlike quality to the eyes.

In the case of the Raphael portrait we must assume that the sitter really had a somewhat misshapen diverging eye. It is unthinkable for an artist to depict a non-existing defect. (A portraitist would rather not show an existing one.) The El Greco portraits are imaginary. According to one of Trevor-Roper's pert remarks, divergence of eyes in this type of "portraiture" is often the result of the artist's affectation rather than of planned realism — an "affectation of otherworldliness." It is a means to express ecstasy — especially if the eyes are also turned upward, or heavenward. In El Greco's case this has become one of the artist's trademark-mannerisms — so much so that his saints sometimes are presented with eyes diverging, unfocused, even when they are depicted looking downward.

In the popular imagination, convergent squint (cross-eyes) reveals some kind of a sinister streak in the character. Not so for the American painter, John Graham. Born a Russian aristocrat, he was a cavalry officer in the Czarist army in World War I. After the 1917 Revolution he escaped, came to America and changed his long Russian name into an American one. He was quite an interesting artist with a lot of psychopathology showing in his work, especially in his nude or almost nude self-portraits that had no lack of *amour propre*. In some of them he presented himself frightfully cross-eyed. Figure 12 is one of these.

Several of his paintings show women with eyes crossed, as in Figures 13 and 14. Inquiries with some of the artist's personal friends (he died in 1961) yield a possible explanation. The artist alluded to the fact that it gave him great satisfaction to watch his partner's eyes while making love. When her eyes started turning inward he knew that they were losing focus, and this for him was a sign of her maximum pleasure. And what about his self-portraits? One can only guess. (Graham was an exciting artist. Some of his portraits carry secret code words or letters. Others indicate his interest in optics and perspective. But all this is beyond our present goal or aim.)

Fig. 12

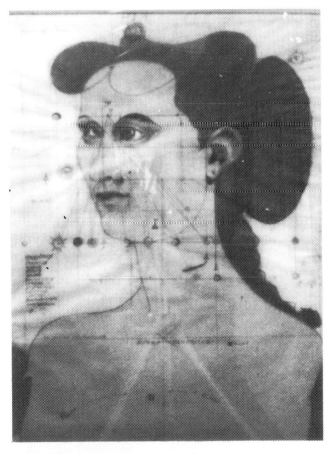

Fig. 13

Fig. 14

Fig. 15

Fig. 16

Fig. 17

Fig. 18

Fig. 19b

Fig. 19a

Notes on the History of Eyeglasses

We can, in a sense, follow the history of the development of eyeglasses by sampling paintings in which eyeglasses are part of the portrayed subject. We do not exactly know when, where, or by whom eyeglasses were invented. Possibly several people invented them. Italy, Florence, *trecento* seem to stake out reasonable claims. In Trevor-Roper's book (previously mentioned) is a photograph of an epitaph on a tombstone in a churchyard in Florence for one "Salvino d'Armato, of the Armati of Florence, inventor of eyeglasses. May the Lord forgive his sins." Was this invention, the author asks half-jokingly, the sin for which forgiveness was asked? The year given on the epitaph is 1317. There is no other evidence that a man by that name ever lived.

J.E.L. (James Lebensohn), the learned contributor of the entry entitled "Eyeglasses" in the 1969 edition of *Encyclopaedia Britannica* does not even mention d'Armato. He names another Florentine, Allessandro di Spina, to whom the introduction of eyeglasses has been attributed. (He also mentions Roger Bacon, the great 13th century scholar, who made the first comment on the optical use of lenses.)

According to Sir Stewart Duke-Elder (whose short historical sketches are not only a pleasure to read but also very accurate) the oldest extant representation of spectacles is to be found in a portrait of Cardinal Hugo of Treviso, in the church of San Nicolo in Treviso, Italy. Duke-Elder's *Textbook of Ophthalmology* (Volume V, Fig. 4502) reproduces a detail of it. The fresco, painted in 1352 by Tommaso da Modena (Fig. 15) is more fully presented in a fine monograph by Baron Ritchie Calder, in a book called *Leonardo and the Age of the Eye.** This book also has two passages (text and drawings reproduced from Leonardo's manuscripts). They should be of some interest to us. In one of them Leonardo explains "how

* Tommaso actually painted two portraits of two clerics reading, but only Cardinal Hugo is wearing spectacles. The other person, Cardinal Nicolas (Fig. 16), is shown using a hand-magnifier. It is quite probable that using a single magnifying lens for reading, actually antedates the invention of spectacles.

eyeglasses aid the sight of the old." The accompanying drawing is very fascinating. With a few changes it could be used in a textbook of today. The other drawing may be representing "a pair of hinged spectacles worn by a man" (Calder adds). (Calder's illustrations are photographs from original, already very time-worn Leonardo manuscripts. It is impossible for me to duplicate them here.)

As far as I can see in the pictorial record, eyeglasses were first used only by older people and only for reading. A fine example for this can be found in an altarpiece (now in Bruges) by Jan van Eyck, the great 15th century Flemish artist (Fig. 17). The painting portrays an elderly cleric with a book and eyeglasses in hand. Those early eyeglasses had to be held by hand in front of the eyes; securing them to the temples or over the ears was a much later development.

The next picture (Fig. 18) shows the artist Pieter Bruegel, the Elder, at work. Behind him we see a connoisseur watching him with eyeglasses somehow fastened to his nose. He does not look too friendly and Bruegel does not either. He evidently did not like the man scrutinizing his painting.

Figure 19a is a detail from Raphael's portrait of Pope Leo X. We see the Pope holding a single lens with a handle. The distribution of the light that is passing through the lens suggests that it is a concave lens. (Raphael must have been a brilliant observer. Dr. Lebensohn also refers to this lens as "concave.") Thus, the Pope must have been nearsighted. Pope Leo X (Fig. 19b) was a Medici, a son of Lorenzo the Magnificent, of a family in which myopia, protruding eyeballs and bad eyesight were endemic.

In one of El Greco's double-portraits of the Saints Peter and Paul (to be discussed later, see Fig. 152), one of them holds a simple lens in hand. Details are not sufficiently clear to tell what kind of a lens it is supposed to be. (The great El Greco was a poor observer. He also did not care much about details.)

Several portraits by Rembrandt show elderly people reading with spectacles precariously perched on the edge of their noses. An especially lovely picture is probably a likeness of the artist's mother. The amazing thing is that none of Rembrandt's eyeglass wearers seems to have taken advantage of an improvement that must have been introduced well before Rembrandt's time. The most famous El Greco portrait (Fig. 20), the likeness of the Grand Inquisitor of Spain (Cardinal Niño de Guevara), is now a prized possession of the Metropolitan Museum of Art in New York City. It was done by El Greco around 1600. (There also exists another portrait of him — also by El Greco.) The great man must have been wearing glasses for seeing — not (or not only) for reading. The lenses are shown fastened around his ears with strings — one of the earliest ways of fixing eyeglasses to the features.

To change the subject, I cannot help seeing myself involved (engulfed) in a problem about which much, probably too much, has already been written — El Greco's alleged "astigmatism." This supposedly would explain those well-known distortions in his renderings of the human

Fig. 20

Fig. 21

Fig. 22

figure, especially in his paintings with a religious theme. One cannot treat this problem lightly or facetiously. I shall have to discuss the nature of El Greco's distortions later and in some detail.

The next two portraits (Figs. 21 and 22) are among my favorites. They are self-portraits by a great 18th century French artist (and I use the epithet "great" sparingly), Jean Baptiste Chardin. In the earlier one, the artist wears an old-fashioned kind of nose-piece; in the later one, the eyeglasses are conveniently attached to some type of jointed temple.

A unique piece of "visual aid" (I have never seen anything similar) is on display in the Hungarian National Museum in Budapest. It is the saber of Arthur Görgey, the commanding general of the forces of the Hungarian Revolution of 1848-49. The visual aid is a convex lens attached with a hinge to the handle of the general's saber. He must have used it to study his maps.

Now, for a change, I want to show (not for artistic, but for ophthalmologic interest) photographs of some well-known personages. The first photograph (Fig. 23) shows Franklin D. Roosevelt and his son, James. They are busy reading. Looking at the picture, we observe two things. The younger man (the one with the eyeglasses) leans forward; he looks through the centers of his eyeglasses; he is obviously nearsighted and young enough to read through his distance-correction lenses. The older person wears a pince-nez (hardly visible in this poor reproduction). It is obvious that he does not bend his head down. His head stays straight and only his eyes are turned downward. He reads through what appear to be bifocals. I like to give a short lecture to patients I want to introduce to their first bifocals. Presenting this worn-out picture, copied from a book of memoirs by the younger Roosevelt, is part of my lecture. "Bifocals are primarily a neck problem, not an eye problem," is my usual comment. One can tell from the way he holds his head that the older man wears some kind of bifocal spectacles.

Here, I think, is the appropriate place to put in a "plug" for trifocals. The second photograph (Fig. 24) is taken from a recent issue of the New York Times (Saturday, January 18, 1975). It shows two well-known senators conversing — Senator John C. Stennis of Mississippi and Senator Frank Church of Idaho. I have shown this picture to several politician-friends and asked their opinion about why the elder of these two gentlemen should be holding his head in such an uncomfortable position. The consensus was that he tries to look down (with some condescension) on the younger man who happens to be taller than he is. I think that the proper explanation is different. Senator Stennis' glasses are obviously bifocals. The upper part of his spectacles does not let him look with comfort upon a face that is too close for sharp focus. He must, therefore, raise his head to look through the lower sections of his spectacles. Had he worn trifocals, he could have saved himself the appearance of snobbishness which this picture seems to suggest.

Of course, photographs can also be works of art — especially photo-portraits. They will, at the same time, also serve as rather accurate, well-dated documents to the history of mores, of apparel, and, also, of eyeglasses, in the century and a half since the invention of photography. Let me refer to the photo-portraits of two young (later famous) Gottingen mathematicians, Minkowski and Hurwitz, taken some time in the last decade of the last century (see Figs. 92 and 93). There is more to be told about them later. But first I have to turn to some other subjects.

Fig. 23

Fig. 24

2 SOME PROBLEMS IN PORTRAITURE

As I turn my eyes on the title of this chapter, I realize that the examples I have so far presented have mostly been portraits. Still, there will be a difference. In the introductory chapter, I spoke about the "what" of examples — what they represent, what some of them might tell, especially tell an ophthalmologist. Now I want to discuss the "how" — some technical problems. I shall start with a painting (Fig. 25) known as "The Artist in his Studio," by Jan Vermeer, the 17th century Dutch painter, of whom not a single portrait is known. This painting is in Vienna's Kunsthistorisches Museum and shows an artist — let us assume it is Vermeer himself — in the act of "doing" a portrait. We see the artist in his studio, but we see only the back of the artist as he sits in front of his canvas and, as we shall see presently, this is the crucial point. Only when presented in this manner can we see the artist *and* his studio in a rational and realistic space-arrangement and only in this manner can we, in our imagination, replace *our* eye for the painter's eye and see that studio the way the painter had seen it. Vermeer, the artist, remains faceless (it is almost symbolic) in the transaction. I, the spectator, see his back only. And I, the spectator, am also faceless. Excluding the interference by mirrors, neither of us can see the other's face and watch the painting being painted at the same time.

Rembrandt also tried (Fig. 26) to show his studio (with a model properly seated, and properly lit) and himself in the process of "doing" her picture. But we cannot possibly imagine *our* eye to be in the place of *his* eye. Rembrandt offered a "surrealist" solution (or better, non-solution) to his project. We cannot see what he saw, and what we see looking at this painting (a model to our left, and a painter on our right) is, no doubt, not what the artist saw. The scenario is impossible, the arrangement is wrong, even if it is a Rembrandt. After all, letting me, the spectator, see what he, the artist, saw (or could have seen) is the very purpose of the visual arts, of the communication between artist and spectator *via* the medium called visual arts. One cannot see one's own face except in a mirror. So Rembrandt must have looked into a mirror while picturing himself. But there is no mirror that could ever produce the sight which he, the artist, tried to make us, the viewers, see. Vermeer, a fine artist, but certainly not of Rembrandt's magnitude, solved this problem in a flash of genius. We can never place ourselves into Rembrandt's place, while — let me repeat this crucial point — there is nothing simpler than placing ourselves (in our imagination, of course) into Vermeer's place in his studio, and see the model and the ambiance (including the source of illumination) with the artist's (Vermeer's) eye.

Fig. 25

Fig. 26

So this is what we see, what Vermeer makes us see: to the artist's left side there is a window, the source of light (with some draperies to manipulate the illumination) and next to the window stands the "model," the person whose picture is being "done." As usual, the easel and canvas are somewhat to the artist's right (this Rembrandt also showed correctly). He holds the brush in the right hand and his right arm rests on a maalstock held by the left hand. (We don't actually see his left hand.)

What we see is the way artists of Vermeer's time (and long before) must have arranged things in a studio since artificial illumination of sufficient intensity was not readily available. It was practically a *necessity* that subject and artist position themselves in this manner. Artists (like the rest of us) are usually right-handed, so the light should preferably come from the left side, directly illuminating the *right* half of the model's face (and body). It is this half that receives straight light, more of the light. On the canvas (I mean the picture surface) this half of the painted face occupies a more leftish position, a place nearer to the left border of the picture-rectangle. (It is a rectangle, usually.) In the arrangement depicted by Vermeer, the painter was sitting somewhat further to the right, farther from the window-side of the picture-space. But this is not always and not necessarily the case. Let me start with a less common example. In a portrait by Frans Hals (Fig. 27) in the Rijksmuseum in Amsterdam, the light still comes from the left side, illuminating the right half of the model's face. But the painter placed himself nearer to the right, toward the left in the picture-space. He saw most of the model's right half-face and his right ear, while the model's eyes were turned toward the right (*his* right) to focus them on the artist. The picture tells us what the arrangement was, from where the light came that illuminated the scene, and where the eye was that looked at it. We can, in general, assume that the source of illumination (e.g., the window), the easel, the canvas and the artist himself retain unchanged positions. We can, in other words, expect that an individual artist will in time have developed some kind of personal ("routine") studio-arrangement. The position of the model will also change very little. (In Vermeer's time it could not be too far from the window.) Artificial illumination was still quite poor at his time. Still, within limits, variations were possible depending on the angle (a) between face and incoming light and (b) between the painter's eye and the pictured space. Thus, looking at the Vermeer painting we could imagine that, without changing position, the model could have turned her face toward the right (*her* right) to face the light, or more toward the left (*her* left) to face the artist. The artist might have at the same time also (and independently) shifted position toward his right or left. Of all alternatives, turning the model's face toward the light seems to be the most common arrangement. (In this case the model's left ear will be in the picture.) But the model's head might also be turned full face into the picture-space. Rarely will the model's head be turned away from the light. (The Frans Hals portrait is such an exception.) "Facing" the artist is generally left to the eyes. (The model will in all these details most likely follow the artist's instructions, as the latter might like one side of the profile better than the other or prefer a certain distribution of light and shadows, etc.)

Fig. 27

Fig. 28a

Fig. 28b

Accordingly, different parts of the model's face will be illuminated and the artist will see more of one or the other side of the head. Also he may see one ear or the other ear or both.

The Vermeer painting is a fine piece by an important artist. I have presented it (a) for the information it gives us on the process of portrait painting, and (b) for letting us understand, even visualize, the magic relationship that exists between the painter's eye and the viewer's eye. As I said earlier, he accomplished all this by a stroke of genius — by placing himself into the picture-space with *his back toward us, his face not seen*. As far as the technique of portrait-painting itself is concerned, the Vermeer piece added nothing revolutionary. His portraits (several of them are double-portraits) are a joy to look at. (Some lovely examples are in the Frick Collection.) Speaking of Vermeer, it is interesting to note that we inadvertently speak about "light," its source, its direction; and about those sun-drenched interiors. We hardly mention such things as windows, doors, furniture, walls with pictures — all presented in a proper geometric setting. Two hundred years after Jan van Eyck, familiarity with the rules of what came to be called "linear" perspective was something taken for granted, hardly worth mentioning. It is the geometry of light — I would like to call it "light"-perspective — that fascinates us in Vermeer's work — the light that in Rembrandt's hands became the supreme storyteller, the primary information-giver. But more than two hundred years earlier Jan van Eyck already documented the fact that there are actually two geometries needed to organize the two-dimensional picture-surface into a tri-dimensional image. Compare Vermeer's "Mistress and Maid" with another double-portrait with ambiance: Jan van Eyck's portrait of a bridal pair (Fig. 28a), done in 1434. You will see that van Eyck, this giant of a painter, already knew it all. This picture is to me the great paradigm of all indoor painting. This is a double-portrait (as it is generally believed) of an Italian merchant, Arnolfini by name, and his bride. We are shown the source of light — a window in the upper left quadrant of the painted surface. Both geometries of the pictorial reproduction of space and its contents are spelled out with unsurpassed clarity. One of them, the geometric technique we today call linear perspective, had in the preceding years made some headway and it was (remarkable coincidence!) codified and presented by the Renaissance genius, Leon Battista Alberti in a book called *Della Pittura* in the years 1435 (in Latin) and 1436 (in Italian) — just a year or two later. This geometric technique, a set of rules, seemed to elevate painting into a science. The other geometry, the rules of the distribution of light had not yet been treated with the same vigor. As far as I can tell, van Eyck first documented in this painting that there is more to a picture than just an assemblage of dots furnished by applying the rules of linear perspective to a picture surface. It is light that gives a kind of unity to the picture, light emanating from a source, light following the geometric rule of rectilinear propagation from that source, light that is falling or not falling on the surface outlined by Albertian linear perspective.*

---

* Of added interest in the Arnolfini portrait is that it shows that the artist was already familiar with the optics of convex mirrors (Fig. 28b).

All this is laid down in the Arnolfini picture. Of course, this painting is still first of all the "portrait" of a room and its contents arranged into an accurately outlined structure of lines running toward a vanishing point. The geometry of illumination is still tentative, even timid. Nevertheless, it is already light, light from a source, directed light, that lends to those contents all that added life. However, I will go into the problems of perspective (both lines and light) later.

Now, I would like to show a series of portraits and I could not start with anything more appropriate than Jan van Eyck's portrait of his wife (Fig. 29), done in 1438 (now in the Municipal Gallery in Bruges). We can "see" that the light was coming from the left side of the picture and illuminated the right half of the subject's face even though we don't actually see a window or other source of light. We can also "see" that the painter must have been sitting further to the right, his right, the picture's right, the model's left. The artist saw the left ear of his model and more of the left half of her face than of the right. Parts of the left half of the face were already in the shade. It is the painting itself that tells us where the light was coming from and where the painter was sitting just as a photograph tells us where the camera's "eye" was positioned.

There is something else remarkable in this portrait — the direction of the eyes. They looked directly at the artist and the artist dared (and was able) to transfer this onto the painted surface. A tremendous innovation! The "Arnolfini" done a mere four years earlier is in this respect still a medieval picture and van Eyck was, in fact, still a medieval man. Whether we count the Middle Ages to 1492, to the year America was discovered (and the Jews expelled from Spain), or to the year 1517 in which Martin Luther nailed his 95 Theses to a church-door in Wittenberg (that is what I was taught in high-school), van Eyck still lived all his life in the Middle Ages. Eyes in medieval paintings did not look at the spectator and the eyes of the two Arnolfinis are not yet either, although the woman looks at the man.

Fig. 29   *Fig.* 30

Fig. 31

Fig. 32

The next example (Fig. 30), is by Raphael, a portrait of Guiliano of the Medicis. It is in the Metropolitan Museum. As we can see the light must have come again from the left, illuminating more of the right half of the subject's face. The artist must have been standing or sitting further to the right. We see the same details as we did in the previous example. They tell us where the painter was positioned relative to the model and where the illumination was coming from. Of course, there are some differences. And, as I have just indicated, van Eyck had still not shed all the artistic traditions of the Middle Ages. Although he already painted in oil, his contrasts of light and shade are still quite restrained. In the Raphael portrait the contrasts are deeper. (Of course, the black beard also adds to the contrast.)

The portrait of the wall-eyed Cardinal Inghirami would fit well here into our enumeration (see Fig. 10). As in the Medici portrait, the light was again coming from the painter's left; and the sitter was turned toward it, exposing more of the left half of his face. Fine shaded areas help in adding to the roundness of face and chin. One can find already in this picture some cast shadows. For example, the writing hand throws a shadow on the paper. (By the way the portrait of the one-eyed musician (see Fig. 4), could also serve here as another example of portrait-painting in what I call the "Vermeer arrangement.")

One cannot see enough of Raphael, so I might just as well show two more of his portraits. One of them (Fig. 31) is the likeness of a Count Castiglione. It is in the Louvre. The other picture (Fig. 32) is in the Prado. This is one of Raphael's most beautiful portraits — the likeness of an unknown Cardinal. There is no need to point out any details of the arrangement. It is quite similar in the two instances. Both sitters appear at an angle to the picture plane, and both turn their gaze toward the artist. In the Cardinal's portrait the turns are sharper and the sideward gaze is more extreme, more conspicuous. Note also the deeper shadows and the sharper outlines of the nose and chin and compare it with the gentle nuances in the Count's face.

There is a reason why I include this less interesting portrait of the Count. Rembrandt saw it at an auction in Amsterdam and it must have impressed him very much, especially the arrangement of the hands. And he must have liked the headgear. He made a quick sketch of the portrait and followed this up with several etchings. One of his best self-portraits (see Fig. 68) is the outcome of experimentations based on his recollection of this portrait. (About this I shall say more later.)

The portrait of Pope Leo X with aids (see Fig. 19b) is an exception to the rule. In this case the light came from the artist's right. This obviously is not a "studio" portrait. The Pope was, we can assume, sitting in one of his chambers and the artist had no choice about the arrangement of the light.

The next two portraits by Rembrandt are somewhat different. (It is hard to make a choice. There are so many great Rembrandt portraits!) In both of the chosen examples it is again the right half of the face that is illuminated by light that must have come from the artist's left. However,

Fig. 35

Fig. 33

Fig. 34

Fig. 36

in the first example, "Portrait of an Oriental," (Fig. 33) in the National Gallery of Art, Washington, D.C., artist and subject faced each other eye to eye. In the second instance (Fig. 34) the subject had turned toward the left (*his* left) side. Thus, the artist saw more of the details of the right half of the face. Of added interest in many of Rembrandt's portraits are the hands. Hands can tell a lot about a person and painting them is difficult. (Not every artist can accomplish this.)

Of course, much more can be said about Rembrandt's accomplishments. Rembrandt, like Bach, was a sleeping volcano — elementary forces hidden under a crust of the most dazzling technical know-how. There will be more to come. Here I only want to mention that Rembrandt obviously was a right-hander and that in the overwhelming majority of his portraits (and self-portraits) the light was — no doubt — coming from *his* left. Whenever light was coming from the right, this was usually and specifically indicated. A good example is his canvas (Fig. 35) in Stockholm, depicting a philosopher next to a large window in the right half of the picture-space. He must have painted it "from life." He was meticulous about details. The source of illumination is also indicated in the well-known painting "The Denial of St. Peter" (Fig. 36) now in the Hermitage. Here the faces are illuminated by a candle covered by the hand of the girl who recognized the apostle.

Using a candle as the apparent source of illumination was almost the trademark of the 18th century French painter, Georges de la Tour (Fig. 37). "The Education of the Virgin" in the Frick Collection, is a lovely example.

The next portrait is that of a handsome young man called Lodovico Capponi by Agnolo Bronzino, in the Metropolitan Museum (Fig. 38). It, too, presents the (by this time) almost generally accepted arrangement of light, subject and artist. The light must have come from the left side of the (one can assume) right-handed artist and illuminated more of the right half of the model's face. Again, as in the van Eyck and the Raphael portraits shown earlier, the artist saw more of the left half of the subject's face.

There is an unusual feature in this portrait and this is why I have chosen to present it — the obvious divergent squint of the model's left eye. Some apparent divergence of the left eye is almost to be expected in this arrangement. As we can see in most of the paintings so far analyzed, models are wont to turn their faces toward the light. Thus, in order to look at the artist they have to turn their eyes toward the left (their left), and, consequently, more of the inside white of their left eyes can be seen. This is a typical and common arrangement in portraiture (once more: model's head turned toward *his* right — toward the light; model's eyes turned toward his left — toward the artist); the inside white of the model's left eye is more conspicuous than that of the right eye. (A glance at Figs. 29 and 30 will confirm this.) Bronzino exaggerated this effect.

The next picture (Fig. 39, now in the Louvre) is a portrait (if, in fact we can call it one) by Leonardo da Vinci. It truly warrants some apologies

Fig. 38

Fig. 39

However, mental association with the just presented portrait by Bronzino will make the choice pardonable. Here we have then the picture of a young male (effeminate — not just handsome), a portrait in a sense, even if nobody was formally "sitting" for it. Kenneth Clark suggests that Leonardo's young, adopted son-servant, the troublesome Giacomo Salai was the model for it and for some similar "portraits" of Leonardo's late period. The subject of this painting manifests a diverging squint of the left eye — again the left eye. The illumination comes mostly from the artist's left side (more accurately the upper left). We will note the typical Leonardoesque cast shadow of the nose upon the lips (the Gioconda smile!); also the distribution of light and shade on the right lower arm of the subject and on his right hand pointing upward. In a way the painting is a "portrait" of St. John the Baptist. However (and you will forgive my insinuation), if we blot out the cross from the subject's hand, we could just as well call it the "portrait" of a more than half-naked prostitute (male or female? — hard to tell) inviting someone with the right forefinger, with a quizzical, half-hidden smile, and with that typical, oblique, dissociated gaze of the trade.

Leonardo was a freethinker and most likely homosexually inclined. (Freud wrote one of his most penetrating studies of psychosexual infantilism based on this aspect of Leonardo's hidden life.) Here we will note again that it is the left eye that apparently had lost focus while the right eye fixates. Artists must have somehow learned that it is usually the right eye that sights. We talk today of right-eye dominance. (Artists knew many things about the eyes, about seeing, that we, physiologists, discovered only much later.) It cannot be mere coincidence that, if any, it is the left eye that appears to diverge in most portraits. This apparent divergence of the left eye is in fact an almost constant feature. It is hard to choose a few examples from so many.

It is my special fondness for the Frick Collection and the vivid memories of its many masterpieces that make me refer to portraits by

Fig. 37

Fig. 40

Fig. 41

Fig. 42

Frans Hals, El Greco and Velázquez to illustrate this. In all three of these portraits the face is turned toward the light coming from the left and the eyes are turned toward the painter, toward the subject's left. The left eye diverges, to a degree, in all three of them — and definitely in the El Greco portrait.

With the painting by Jean Baptiste Camille Corot (Fig. 40) in the Clark Art Institute of Williams College, we arrive at the last century. And it is still the same arrangement. Once again we can see that the light was coming from the artist's left and illuminated the right half of the model's face. The artist saw and registered more details of the left half of her face as she was sitting to his left. She was looking at the painter with eyes turned toward the left (*her* left). Once again, the artist saw more of the inside white of the left eye.

The next picture is by an unknown primitive artist (Fig. 41). It is a childhood portrait of Ignac Semmelweis, the great and tragic 19th century Hungarian physician, the saviour of mothers from the ravages of childbed fever. The original is in the Medical-Historical Museum in Budapest.

A "primitive" artist is usually one who knows what is "real" — real, not an appearance. He ignores shadows, *chiaroscuro*, or the changes of color with changes of light. He "knows" that the two halves of a face have the same color all across — the same "real" color. He uses his knowledge, not his eyes. To us, the sophisticated ones, such portraits appear "flat." (And so do Japanese or Byzantine portraits which we have nevertheless learned to admire.)

Of course, the classic arrangement prevailed even in the work of our "primitive" artist. We shall assume that he was right-handed, and that his light too must have come from the left side. So he too saw more of the left half of his model's face. And since the young man must have been sitting near the window and turned his gaze at the artist, we note here too more of the inside white of the left eye.

One can hardly imagine any greater contrast than that between this painting by an unknown primitive (flat — but for our sophisticated taste not at all displeasing) and the Mona Lisa (Fig. 42) by Leonardo da Vinci. (She is now in the Louvre in Paris.) The essential features of the Vermeer arrangement are once again seen here — the general direction of the light (did he in public also use the left hand?), the turn of the head, the turn of the gaze, the inside white of the left eye.

Leonardo was not only an artist, he was also a scientist, intrigued about so many things, by the geometry of lights and shadows. He classified shadows as being of two kinds, cast shadows and surface shadows, and assigned each a different role in his endeavor to transfer reality onto the picture surface. He noted that shadows can intermingle, that multiple shadows can be cast by the same object as light from a window hits the object under slightly different angles. It is, I think, this arrangement of multiple shadows cast by the nose upon the mouth (the upper lip) that causes the unique and particular shimmering over the mouth which we call the "Gioconda smile."

3 SELF-PORTRAITS

Fig. 43

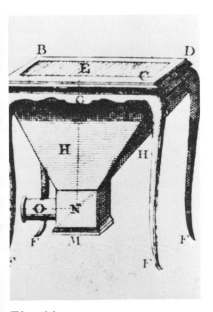

Fig. 44

Fig. 45

Of all the faces in the Universe one's own is the only face one cannot actually ever see. So the artist has to look into a mirror if he wants to draw or paint an image of himself — specifically, an image of his own face. Usually, though not necessarily, the artist will use a plane mirror; a plane mirror upright. Thus, whatever *he* sees, whatever *we* see, in the mirror will be upright and undistorted. It is this whatever-he-sees or whatever-we-see within the confines of the mirror that we call the "mirror-image." The self-portraitist's job is to "transfer" (carry over) this image onto his paper or canvas. It is the "transferred" image of the "mirror"-image of "self" that we call "self-portrait." The mirror itself is not usually included into the self-portrait. Nor is (I will show some rare exceptions) the hand that draws or paints with which the artist is drawing or painting. He is, besides, all on his own. There are some optical devices (e.g., the *camera obscura*) with the help of which the image of any other person or thing can be projected upon, and outlined on, a screen or translucent paper. I (as an outside viewer) can see the model, the artist and the optical device between them (Figs. 43 and 44). They are all in my visual space. But the artist cannot ever see himself through such a device. Optical scientists call the "mirror"-image "virtual" as opposed to "real." It is in a kind of "negative" space.

So there are some problems to self-portraiture. I still remember the occasion that prompted me to analyze them in a somewhat systematic manner. I was confronted by a painting of Frans Hals (Fig. 45) in the Frick Collection. That must have been at least 25 years ago. Even by that time I had seen it many times. It intrigued me because it is one of those paintings that has eyes that follow the viewer from one end of the room to the other. But that is a different story. When I first saw it, it was labelled as "Portrait of *the* Artist." Recently, I noticed the label had been changed to "Portrait of *an* Artist." (The italics are mine.) Not knowing anything about problems of documentation I kept on presuming it to be a self-portrait and it was on this presumption that I started my analysis. It was not documentary evidence I was looking for. I could not have added an *iota* to the learned discussion of pro's and con's in the collection's magnificent catalogue.

The first thing I was looking for was the direction of the light. There are three more portraits by Hals in the Frick Collection. Thus, it could be easily verified that the light seemed to come from the left whether the "model" was someone else or the artist himself.

As we have already discussed, light in the process of portrait-painting usually comes from the artist's left side. It primarily illuminates the right half of the model's face and this right half of face appears, *on the canvas*, nearer the left border of the picture-space. But how about self-portraits? Obviously, there is no model in the stricter sense of the word, and what matters is that in this case the source of light illuminates the left half of the artist's own face. This left half of his face (and body) must have appeared to our artist as being nearer to the left border of the mirror. On the canvas (in the "painted" image of the "mirror"-image) this arrangement was duplicated. Thus, in a self-portrait the *painted image of the left half of the artist's face occupies a position nearer the left border of the canvas*. And it is this half of the face that to the artist must have appeared better illuminated (provided the light came from the left). Thus, the distribution of light is also "transferred." The other half-face, nearer to the right border of the canvas, is in the shade.

All what I have said so far about this self-portrait (if it is a self-portrait) is generally valid. There are, of course, some variables. The artist might have turned his face (or body) out of the mirror's plane, letting light fall more or less onto the essentially shaded half of the face. All this needs no discussion. One fact is evident: as long as the light comes from the left it makes no difference whether the artist paints a self-portrait or someone else's portrait. It is the half of the face that appears nearer to the left border of the canvas that appears better illuminated. As far as being a self-portrait *this detail offers no clue*.

Let us rather take a look at the arrangement of hands in the Hals portrait. (We shall still assume it is a self-portrait, not a portrait of one painter by another painter.) While the artist was doing it, he (more likely than not) held a palette in his left hand. At first glance (and especially to the less-sophisticated observer), the mirror-image of a left hand looks like an ordinary right hand (someone else's right hand!) and so does its replica — the transferred image on the canvas. A palette in this "right"-looking hand would therefore suggest that the artist is left-handed. And this, for whatever reason, might not be to the artist's liking. Thus, palettes hardly appear in self-portraits, at least in undoctored self-portraits. Without a palette, the mirror-image of the left hand is much more acceptable as a "right" hand. But some cheating will be helpful, even permissible. So our good Frans Hals added a brush to the transferred image of his left hand making it look even more like a "right" hand. (It is even conceivable that he actually placed a brush into his left hand *while* outlining its image with his right.) But there is more to this. Since the artist was painting with his right hand, he was unable to see this hand in the mirror *while* he was actually painting. And, anyway, whenever (in painting pauses) he *could* see his right hand *in* the mirror, it looked like a "left" hand. And the more so, since this painting hand inevitably held some utensil *while* he worked.

Fig. 46

Fig. 47

Fig. 48

Killing two birds with one stone, solving the problem the easiest way, our artist blithely painted some imaginary drapery around this problem-giving arm and hand. ("No offense, no problem," he must have thought. Or maybe: "Problem solved.") In any event, my feeling is that unless uncontestable documentary evidence exists to the contrary, this picture must be labelled a self-portrait. And that *intrinsic evidence* is of importance in the face of any doubt. *This Hals painting makes no sense if it is not a self-portrait.*

Hals was certainly not the first artist who tried to paint a self-portrait and not the first to note the problem of hands. He was a great painter but not a great thinker. He wanted to paint a self-portrait but he also wanted to avoid complexities. So he made a right hand out of his left hand by painting a brush into its canvas-image and he avoided the problem which the painting right hand presents, a problem which (as we shall see) a more brooding, more philosophizing, more Germanic and much much greater predecessor, Albrecht Dürer, finally also left unsolved. I don't know if Hals was the first to use this drapery trick. (I like to call it the "Frans Hals trick.") And he certainly had some followers. One, a well-known painter (not a deep thinker but a facile problem-solver), was Anthony Van Dyke. His self-portrait in Munich (Fig. 46) offers a good example of this drapery trick. (I especially dislike the boneless hand in his lap.) Another artist (from whom I cannot withhold some grudging admiration) is the famous court-painter of King Louis XIV: Hyacinthe Rigaud. He invented some kind of a double-twist to the drapery trick. He loved to paint sumptuous outfits and he must have had a good sense of humor. In one of his self-portraits (Fig. 47, in Karlsruhe) he draped away the image of the right arm and hand in the Frans Hals manner. Nothing spectacular. The mirror-image of the left hand looks, of course, like a right hand, but it does not show too much activity since palette and brush rest on a table. The other, the Uffizi self-portrait (Fig. 48), is unique. Among the hundreds of self-portraits I have analyzed in many years, I have never come across a reversed Frans Hals trick. In this instance our artist draped away the image of his left arm and hand — not that of the right — and he painted an image of his *right* hand as it appeared to him in the mirror (but let me add: *not while* painting. Inevitably, he made himself look left-handed. Was he, by any chance? Or was he ambidextrous? (There is a portrait of Rigaud in the Philadelphia Museum, drawn or copied by an artist, about whom I know nothing, called Brevet. I wish I had a chance to study it.)

My paradigm for the portrait of a right-handed painter by *another* painter is a beautiful picture by El Greco, the portrait of an unknown painter (see Fig. 140) in a Seville museum. The subject holds a brush in his right hand (the hand nearer the left border of the canvas). We see the palm-side of this hand. He is shown ready to apply the brush. (I shall say more about this portrait in Chapter VI.)

Fig. 49

Fig. 50

Anthonis Mor

The two self-portraits of the 16th century painter Anthonis Mor (also known as Sir Anthony More and Antonio Moro) in the Phaidon volume* of *Self-Portraits* have been a puzzlement to me for quite a while. They are beautiful (this is the right word). Portrait #129 in the Phaidon volume (Fig. 49) is a stunning picture of a man of great charm and elegance. The eyes look searchingly at the viewer. The outfit — the heavy golden double chain, the handles of sword and dagger, the hunting dog — everything exquisite. And those hands! The hand nearer the left border of the canvas (the image of the left hand, if this is a self-portrait) is maybe not quite correct in its anatomy — the thumb bends somewhat too far backward. The other hand, as much as one can see of it, could not be nicer. It seems to play with the dog. Seldom will one see hands as well done as this artist did. The general impression is of an impeccable portrait in the style of the master-painter Anthonis Mor. *But nothing tells me that it is a self-portrait!* Mor must have been at home in the courts of Europe. He was knighted in England after painting a portrait of Queen Mary I, Henry VIII's unhappy daughter. (The *Encyclopaedia Britannica* calls it Mor's "masterpiece," and what a dazzling presentation of royal robes it is!) He finally became court-painter to King Philip of Spain. Mor loved to portray important people in their finest attire. Figure 49 represents, I think, one of them.

* In addition to slides, catalogues, cut-outs from newspapers and magazines, my chief aids to memory for preparing this chapter are a book called *Fünfhundert Selbstporträts* (Five Hundred Self-Portraits) all in black and white, published by Phaidon Press in Vienna in 1935; also, a book called *Self-Portraits*, an English translation of a volume edited by Manuel Gasser and published by Appleton-Century in 1961. I also have some other Phaidon volumes at hand — among them the Bredius Catalogue of Rembrandt's paintings and the great Waetzoldt biography of Dürer. They were written in German and published in Vienna up to and including 1936. My Phaidon "El Greco" is in English and was published in Great Britain in the ominous year of 1938. *Habent sua fata libelli.* And so do publishing houses. Phaidon Press started in Germany in those glorious Weimar days. Some time after 1934 it moved for a short time to Vienna. It started its new life in Great Britain and New York. There is no more to be said. And what this means should not be forgotten.

The other painting (Fig. 50; #130 in the Phaidon volume) is of greater interest. I had a chance to see and study it at a memorable exhibit, "Bruegel and his Century," in Brussels in the 1960's (on loan from the Uffizi in Florence). It is — we are told — a portrait of *the* painter, obviously the portrait of *a* painter. I realize that here I am sticking out my neck much too far. I don't have the expert knowledge to speak about the canvas, the paint, the *minutiae* of brush strokes which would certify that this is a portrait by Mor's hand. All I can say is that this is the portrait of a painter because (a) what in a "non-self-portrait" would pass as the left hand is holding a palette, and (b) the subject is shown sitting in front of an easel and an empty canvas. It certainly looks like a painting by Mor. It is the portrait of an important personage with the gestures one associates with Mor's work and again the wonderful hands he usually painted. The turn of the head is the same as that in the just discussed portrait; the eyes look very much the same. Much of the body's posture is similar to that of the other portrait. However, the whole figure is shorter (the man is sitting). He seems altogether somewhat more plump. The little curl at the hairline is missing. The hand near the left border (the purported right hand of the person portrayed) rests comfortably on the subject's thigh. (But, mark it, this hand holds no brush!) The other hand holds the palette, the maalstock and the brushes. The figure is turned toward the right, toward an otherwise empty canvas which occupies a considerable part of the picture-space. There is no reason to suspect that this is not the portrait of the painter. But was it done by Mor himself? (Or was it *all* done by him?) There is a *trompe l'oeil* piece of wrinkled paper painted onto the otherwise empty canvas. Perfect! (Note the pin that seems to fasten the paper to the canvas: one would swear it is a real pin.) This paper tells, in Greek, in the words of a famous contemporary scholar, that this is "a portrait of the noble artist, Mor, the way he saw himself in a mirror." The picture is signed by Mor and is dated "a. 1559" and it once again reassures us that it was done *ipsa manu*. It must be true. It must be his portrait. But how did he do it? It is a marvel.

The Brussels exhibit presented several other portraits from European galleries by Mor. There are two at the Rijksmuseum. They are all beautiful, and all the same. The same posture, the same gentle turn of body and head toward the right border of the canvas (the female portrait turns the other way), the same turn of the eyes toward the left border, all looking at the artist. They have the same or almost the same disposition of hands. All lovely. Exquisite textiles, accessories. Same, almost standardized illumination, fine shadows cast by a gently curved, slightly aquiline nose. But not much searching of soul. It almost looks as if this wonderful artist-technician would have had one schema, with minor variations, for all. He obviously was a busy painter (he was royal court-painter of Philip II of Spain), and his subjects were most likely also busy people. The catalogue of his portraits in Hyman's biography reads like a *Who's Who* of 16th century royalty and *entourage*. Maybe his subjects were just sitting for their features while the rest, the garments, the hands, and the paraphernalia were added using the same routine and the same

Fig. 51

Fig. 52

model. As we can expect, Mor would not leave out important details, e.g., the Order of the Golden Fleece in the Duke of Alba's portrait. He is presented in full armor and still fits into the Mor scheme. Mor's self-portrait with easel and palette does certainly not reproduce what he saw in the mirror. He must have had someone else "sit-in" while he painted those exquisite hands — the "right" hand resting on his thigh as in most of the other routine portraits and the "left" hand holding the tools of the trade in a manner he could never have seen them in the mirror. According to a short paragraph on Mor in the Brussels catalogue, it is the first self-portrait of a painter using the props of the trade. Yes, they are all there. But why is there no brush, not a single brush, in the right hand? Did "the noble artist Mor" not see the problem self-portraiture presents? Or did he just not bother? He obviously did not portray what he saw.

Rubens, that great Rubens, was born in 1577. (Europe recently celebrated his anniversary.) I have never learned to appreciate him. Mor probably died the same year. (Different sources give 1576 or 1577.) Was his soul reincarnated in Rubens? (I know that this is a grossly unfair comparison.) Or was it Titian's? (He also died around the same time.) Surely self-portraits offered no problem to Rubens. But nothing else did either. The question with Ruben's self-portraits is again: How did or could he do it? I have not given it enough thought or study.

The same holds, I confess, for one of the two well-known self-portraits by Titian (Fig. 51.) The optics of mirror-images makes me believe that a self-portrait cannot be a straight "profile." That famed and truly beautiful self-portrait of the old master (in the Prado) is a profile (almost a profile). I don't know how he did it. (The problem of double mirrors would have to be investigated. But that too must be left to someone else.) The other Titian self-portrait is in Berlin (Fig. 52). Gasser, describing it, mentions the "resting" right hand when, obviously, the hand he is referring to is the one nearer to the left border of the canvas — the transferred mirror-image of the artist's left hand. He also treats the other hand in a similar confused and confusing manner. It is a pity — a serious flaw in an otherwise fine book.

Fig. 53

Fig. 54

Albrecht Dürer, Junior

Any serious study of problems of self-portraiture must deal with Dürer, especially his two penned self-portraits (Figs. 53 and 54). Dürer was one of the greatest draftsmen of all times. As far as I can tell, he tried harder than anyone before his time to duplicate what he saw of himself in a mirror. Let us first look at the eyes in these two drawings done in his early twenties. We shall see that more of the inside white of the left eye (of the transferred replica of the mirror-image of the left eye) is visible. And herewith it started — all that literature (mostly German) about the *Dürer-Blick,* the *wall-eyed* Dürer.

The first of the two drawings (Fig. 53), indicates how the artist saw himself in a mirror (obviously drawing with the right hand, which we do not see), and trying for some reason to cover his diverging left eye with his left hand. One German ophthalmologist actually suggested that the artist attempted to cover one eye because he was wall-eyed and had double-vision, but to my *ennui* he told us that the artist tried to cover his divergent *right* eye with the *right* hand — which, to say the least, is incorrect. What we see in the drawing is what Dürer saw in the mirror: the image of his *left* eye, partially covered by the image of the *left* hand. (Dürer was a Renaissance man. He already knew about the schism between appearance and reality and he tried to catch and to perpetuate the former — the appearance — not reality.) We will, by the way, note how overly large and long this hand is in comparison with the face. This is not on account of any astigmatism. Dürer, well acquainted with the rules of linear perspective, tried to draw what he actually saw. Since his hand and its mirror-image were necessarily nearer to the mirror than his face or eye, the hand (the mirror-image of it) must have appeared larger, longer than his face. He drew exactly what he saw in linear perspective: nearer as larger; as he *saw* it, not as he *knew* it.

In the second of the two self-portrait drawings (Fig. 54) we will, at first, note some of the same details. If we look carefully (very carefully) we can see that the light came from the artist's left in both instances (the artist was, obviously, not really interested in rendering this accurately), and illuminated the left half of his face (which in the drawings *looks like* anybody else's right half face and is nearer the left border of the paper). Again, and in both instances, more of the inside white of this eye is visible. (It is, of course, the mirror-image of the diverging left eye.) But this time

— so it seems to me — Dürer wanted to accomplish something much more difficult. He wanted to draw an image of his own right hand "in" the mirror — and while drawing. This he must have found to be impossible. As far as I can tell, this drawing is the first attempt by a (right-handed) self-portraitist to show how his own right hand appeared to him in the mirror at a moment he was not actually drawing but ready to draw. That was the best he could do. He had to use the mirror. Thus, the spatial schizophrenia is inevitable: he drew what *looked* like a left hand — anybody else's left hand.

The difficulties of seeing one's drawing hand in a mirror *while drawing* are almost insurmountable. The face, the other hand, the other arm, are (or can be) parts of a mirrored panorama; they have their stable positions in the mirror-space and in its transferred replica — the picture-space. But the drawing hand is constantly on the move. (We will note that the mirror-image of the drawing hand is again much too big for its esthetic integration with the pictured hand. The artist's hand was obviously again closer to the mirror than his head. So the retinal image of the hand's mirror-image was really larger.) We cannot fail to notice that the image of this hand in the drawing is not part of the composition, of the total design. It is not part of the mirrored panorama. It stands in itself; it is "there," but independent, unconnected, just like that "thing" (a pillow, of all things) that for some reason occupies the lower half of the drawing. (There are several other pillow-studies on the back of the paper.)

We can say that, in a sense, the artist saw his right hand, his drawing hand, twice — and in two spaces. At one moment he saw it in the mirror — more accurately in the mirrored space — a fleeting appearance which he wanted to perpetuate. But then, just a moment later, as his hand and gaze inevitably turned toward the drawing board, he also saw this hand — another kind of a hand, a hand in his normal kinesthetic space — and he saw it drawing; a *real* hand, "felt" as well as "seen." As I just said it was the first one of the two images, the mirror-image of his right hand, which Dürer tried to "transfer" from the unreachable space behind Alice's looking glass into the reality of the picture-surface and to *immobilize it into the reality of contours* (this is what the word "drawing" means) with his *real* hand, on *real* drawing paper, in the *real* sensori-motor space of his *real* self. But he did not fully succeed. He concentrated all his attention on the hand in the mirror, a strange hand of which we see the palm-side with the thumb and first two fingers in some strange and cramped position, distorted and disproportionate and certainly not of the quality of the famous and fabulous "Praying Hands" (one of the dozen odd masterpieces Dürer created). Pity that he did not retain the pen, his drawing utensil, in the drawing! The reason seems obvious. He must have realized that retaining the pen would have made him look definitely left-handed (as his future more formal painted self-portraits tell us) and this he had wanted to avoid. Dürer never came to grips with the problem of this "ghost" again. The image of his active right hand in mirrored space looked too much like an active left hand in the portraits of other people. So our young giant compromised. The pressure not to appear a southpaw was too great.

Fig. 55

Fig. 56

More About Self-Portraits. Left and Right in the Picture Space

In the centuries that followed Dürer, quite a few artists have tried to integrate the mirror-image of their arms and hands into the picture-space of their self-portraits. There are several ways to accomplish this. In some instances the apparent left-handedness is quasi-hidden: the drawing implement *de facto* held by the right hand is replaced by some neutral object which could be held by either hand. Some cheating is unavoidable. But at least the artist does not look like he is painting with a "left" hand.

An interesting example is a self-portrait by the prominent German painter Max Liebermann, a good and accomplished (if not great) artist whose long career stretches well into our present century.

In Figure 55 we see Liebermann in his studio in a long, white painter's coat and surrounded by *paraphernalia* that place him in his studio. We see a part of a mirror and we see the back of the artist's bald head in this mirror. Note that his figure (as much as can be seen of it) appears to cover part of the mirror (*this* mirror). This adds quite a bit to our illusion that the portrait we are looking at is not a mere mirror-image but closer to his *real* self as seen by other people.

As far as the hands in this portrait are concerned, the "right" looking left hand was easily disposed of: it disappeared into one of the artist's pockets. His figure turns out of the mirror-plane. His right hand was farther from this mirror and, therefore, its image in the mirror has appeared smaller, not only farther. It is a rather poorly designed hand. (After all, it is also just memorized like Dürer's hand.)

Dürer's painful problem, i.e., to show the mirror-image of a painter's painting right hand in that crucial moment just after seeing it but just before painting it, is solved by Liebermann in a most elegant manner. We see the image of the hand on the canvas (just the way the artist saw it in the mirror which we do not see — but in which he saw himself). His thumb and the first two fingers are still holding something. But it is not what he really saw. It is a cigarette, not the brush. The person presented on the canvas is a gentleman who happens to hold a cigarette. He holds it in a "left"-looking hand. "Self-Portrait with Cigarette" by Max Liebermann (painted when he was around sixty years old) is one of the most satisfactory solutions for the great right-hand dilemma. Satisfactory and not without charm.

Fig. 57

Fig. 58

There also exists an older version of the "Self-Portrait with Cigarette." In Figure 56, we see the artist in an arrangement that reminds me of Mor with the right-looking left hand resting on his thigh, while the other, the left-looking right hand holds a cigarette.

The reason why I found it worthwhile to tarry with this picture is the strange location of the breast-pocket of the artist's coat. Male or female, the breast-pocket (if any) of our coats, shirts, jackets are on the left side. The reason for this arrangement is, most likely, the easier access by the right hand. This being the case, in portraits and photographs the breast-pocket is necessarily nearer to the right border of the picture-space. In self-portraits it must be nearer to the left border. From this it follows that a breast-pocket nearer to the left border of the picture-space earmarks a portrait as a self-portrait.

The next picture (Fig. 57) is still another self-portrait by Liebermann. A charming work of art of almost sophisticated simplicity, trimmed of problems. We do not see much of the left arm and nothing of the left hand, while the right hand is kept out of sight altogether. The easel and canvas intrude upon the mirror-space. We concentrate upon the beautifully painted face, the romantic hat, the understated wearing apparel. We do not miss what we do not see. A fine painting. The figure is not centered. Most of it is in the left half of the picture-space, hardly leaving any room for the left arm and none for the left hand.

Fig. 59

Fig. 60

Liebermann also tried the impossible: to see his right hand in the mirror *while* painting and still keep it within the space of the mirror-image. The result is a picture (Fig. 58) that is, to say the least, grotesque and certainly without any esthetic merit. The artist had to arrange mirror and canvas at some odd angles to each other. He had to break his neck to see himself, to see his eyes, and to see his painting right hand resting against the maalstock. Note how the wrist is all distorted and in the wrong place altogether. True, he could finally see the easel and the painting arm all within the mirror and also his left hand holding the palette. Of course, he looked left-handed. He looked left-handed to himself and that is the way he does to us too. And this apparent left-handedness is not only awkward, it is also over-emphasized. His elbow almost hits you in the nose. Pitiful. Ugly. Wasted effort.

The Hungarian painter Csontváry did better (Fig. 59). He also manipulated easel and mirror, but by turning the Liebermann-arrangement by 180 degrees he was able to bring the image of his right arm into the background of the picture-space. It is the palette that is now in the foreground. The drawing hand (it looks like a "left" hand) is now really seen drawing; it is holding a crayon. The window, the outdoors are integrated into the picture-space. It all adds up to a strange but altogether not unpleasant composition. The canvas (its obverse side!) reaches now into the mirror-space. The one thing that is still grotesque is the position of the eyes. The artist had to turn his eyes into an extreme position in order to crowd himself (right arm and hand included) and even some of his canvas into the mirrored space.

One of the most charming, unobtrusive, and yet sophisticated little masterpieces (it is small even in its dimensions) is the self-portrait by one of Rembrandt's pupils, the Dutch artist Gerard Dou (Fig. 60) in the Rijksmuseum. This lovely painting is also a refined example of *trompe l'oeil*. A hanging curtain covers almost one third of the canvas. A curtain rod on which it hangs runs across its top. The curtain appears to leave a niche visible — the entrance to it illuminated by light that must come from the spectator's left. It obviously came from the artist's left. The shadow cast by the subject upon the wall of the niche confirms this. Some dark drapery in its background adds depth — Rembrandt's undefined depth — to the niche. The *trompe l'oeil* effect is enhanced by the never-too-old trick of having a book protrude beyond the lower front border of the niche and by adding a piece of paper with a crumpled corner (both casting shadows down and right). The subject's hand that is nearer the left edge of the canvas could be a model's resting right hand. But since this is a self-portrait it must be the mirror-image of his (not painting) left hand. It is the *other* hand that makes this little painting so remarkable to me. The artist must have seen the palm of his right (painting) hand in the mirror — of his right hand holding some painting utensil. This utensil our artist turned into a pipe. Our feelings do not object to a person's holding a pipe (there were no cigarettes yet) in an upturned left-looking hand. It was truly just the merest minimum of cheating that was necessary to make this self-portrait acceptable to a right-handed 17th century world.

More About the Dürers— Father and Son

Once more I return to the dramatic Dürer story. There is a prologue to it and a postlude. The Albertina, the great Vienna collection of prints, has a silverpoint drawing by Dürer done when he was 13 years old. (A later notation by Dürer's own hand attests to the accuracy of the claim.) It is a self-portrait — his first of several (Fig. 61). The eyes are still medieval — not focused on the viewer, not focused on anything. The mirror-image of the left arm and hand is drawn in fine detail. (Note the forefinger pointing.) The mirror-image of the right sleeve is more hesitantly done and there is no image of the right hand. What the young Dürer some eight years later could not handle, the child Dürer had handled with amazing delicacy. His "solution" is at least as good as that by Hals. Did he invent it? Did he learn it? I have no way to decide.

Fig. 61

There is a companion piece (another silverpoint drawing) in the Albertina which seems to be accepted as a portrait of Albrecht Dürer *senior*, the journeyman goldsmith from Hungary who after years on the road finally settled in Nuremberg to become the father of a famous son. The Phaidon volume of self-portraits lists this drawing under #21 and dates it "around 1480." If it is a self-portrait then we must consider it a major accomplishment worthy of special notice (Fig. 62). Yes, if this drawing is a transferred mirror-image (the definition of "self-portrait"!) then it follows that (a) it is the left hand's mirror-image which is shown holding a statuette (maybe the type of *objets d'art* Dürer *senior* used to make to earn a living), while (b) the image of the right hand, of the drawing hand, is artfully eliminated. Artfully — not as grossly as Frans Hals did it. So, if this is a self-portrait done by Dürer *senior* "around 1480" then his young son (who was 13 years old in 1484) could have learned the trick from his father. The German Dürer-expert, W. Waetzoldt, lists this same drawing as a pen portrait of the father done by Dürer *junior,* the child prodigy, around 1486 — which is two years *after* he did his own authenticated self-portrait. If this is the case then the portrait of Dürer *senior* was not done *via* a mirror, and the hand that holds the statuette is the sitter's right hand. But why is the image of the left hand covered up? (I raise the question; I cannot provide the answer.) I have never studied the pertinent documentation; however, intrinsic evidence tells me that the portrait of Dürer *senior* is a self-portrait and, as a senior citizen myself, I am ready to concede to a minor artist (Dürer *senior*) some small slice of the education of his great son.

Fig. 62

Fig. 63

Fig. 64

To those two earlier discussed pen-and-ink drawings of the 21 or 22-year-old Dürer (we do not call him *junior*), we add a third one (Fig. 63), also in the Albertina. It presents three sketches of the artist's left hand and arm. This drawing is no less puzzling. But maybe we can unravel its meaning. Here we have young Dürer struggling. He is trying (as I see him) to solve the great problem (a problem that will now be almost solved, I think, for the first time in art history), i.e., the "hand" problem of self-portraiture and especially the right hand's problem; the problem to integrate an acceptable image of the artist's own working right hand into the picture-space. I have, of course, no documentary evidence for what I try to say here. I can merely try to imagine from the pictorial evidence what could have run through Dürer's mind. And as I see it, he did finally find a suitable arrangement even if he did not find a solution. He found out that the left hand (the *real* left hand — not the mirror-image of the left hand!) could serve as a model, a cartoon, for a hand fitting into a self-portrait. It could provide an acceptable image *in lieu* of the *right* hand's image since (as Dürer had found out) the image of this hand is not only evasive (it disappears from the mirrored space whenever the real right hand draws a line or applies the brush), but it also appears to be a left hand anyway. And for this there is no remedy. Anyone who looks at a self-portrait picture, without further analysis of the kind here suggested, will always "see" a left hand in the self-portrait though it is a right hand's painted image.

At about the same time, Dürer worked on his first painted self-portrait (Fig. 64, now in the Louvre). This was the first of his three well-known painted self-portraits done in the grand manner. It is the masterpiece of a young man (about 23 years old) who suddenly bloomed into a master. About illumination I shall say nothing. About the position of the eyes not much has to be said. We encounter that typical *Dürer-Blick*. The eye we see deviating is the transferred image of the mirror-image of the artist's left eye. The image of the left hand and arm presents the first, but smaller problem and if our speculation is correct then this problem was already solved by Dürer *senior*. In fact, no great imagination is needed to recover, in the painted image of the artist's left arm and hand, a replica from his father's self-portrait. As we look at it, it looks like a right hand (I mean arm and hand), an inactive right hand, a "holding" rather than a "doing" right hand. In the father's case it was a statuette it held. Here it is a thistle. But then there is another hand near the lower right corner of the canvas. It looks like a left hand though it must be the image of a right hand for the portraiture of which our young master found yet no working solution. What I offer now as a possible explanation is pure psycho-history. Still here it is: There are three sketches in the last mentioned pen-and-ink drawing (see Fig. 63). The two sketches on the right depict peculiar, seldom-met views of the inside, the palm-side of the left hand of the artist's own, felt-and-seen (real) left hand (not of a mirror-image). He must have had some reason for this. And we do not have to do much imagining to satisfy ourselves that these two sketches of the artist's real left hand are not unlike that mystery hand in Figure 54, that disappearing and reappearing image of the right hand which the artist tried to nail to

Fig. 65

the paper as he had just seen it in the mirror. Maybe he used these two drawings as cartoons to add some stability to that evanescent image of the right hand.

In a moment I will talk about the third sketch — another view of the artist's real left hand and its possible significance as a prop to improve on the image of the right hand in self-portraiture. But first a note: Some geometric imagination is needed to see that real images of one's left hand and appropriate mirror-images of one's right hand are congruous patterns. (Congruous means "superposable" without removal from the two dimensions of a plane.) It might also be necessary to remind the reader that our own two hands, ears, gloves, shoes, etc. are incongruous and so are their respective images and mirror-images.

In the third Dürer sketch (see Fig. 63), if we cut out an appropriate part of the sketch and rotate this part clockwise about 100 degrees we shall find that this cut-out hand and that inconspicuous left-looking hand in the lower right corner of the painted portrait are essentially "superposable." There is one more minor item: Dürer placed a small flower (the thistle) into the hand of this sketch. He obviously experimented while he painted. (The sketches of the left hand and the first painted self-portrait were most likely done the same year.) He placed the same thistle into the right-looking image of his left hand, so that this "right"-looking hand would have something to do. The other painted hand rests in the corner, inconspicuous, somehow holding onto the other end of the thistle. Anyway, my story would at least give an explanation for the existence of those three strange sketches. Somehow the presence of the thistle in both the painted portrait *and* the sketches makes it at least conceivable that some cross-fertilizing relationship did exist. But it is not a happy or an easy solution. It is difficult to see the connection if one is lacking geometric imagination. I don't know of anybody who would have adopted the method. At the same time, the transformation of the mirror-image of the left hand into a "right"-looking hand (sometimes it is also resting on a kind of balcony) remains an everlasting contribution of Dürer *senior* to the history of self-portrait painting.

The self-portrait we have just discussed (see Fig. 64) is the earliest among the painted formal self-images of Dürer. It shows a Dürer grown up, a Dürer matured and, in a sense, a Dürer defeated. (Make your choice.) I don't think (and I know his *oeuvre* quite well) that he ever again attempted to draw his right hand into the picture-space. Even in his famous self-portrait, the "Christ" portrait in Munich (Fig. 65), Dürer did not try anymore to integrate any kind of image of his right hand into the design. All we see is the transferred right-looking mirror-image of the left hand. We don't really miss the other arm and hand. The light came from the artist's left. (Note the shadow that covers one side of the nose.) We find it natural that we see fewer details on the side that is away from light.

More About Rembrandt and More About Self-Portraits

Let us start with a self-portrait presumably by Rembrandt, in the de Young Museum in San Francisco (Fig. 66). The question is whether it is by Rembrandt. In the Bredius Catalogue it follows a practically identical self-portrait now in Dresden (Fig. 67). In the newer, more critical Bauch Catalogue it is not mentioned. Neither is it to be found in the 1956 Pinder monograph called *Rembrandt Selbstbildnisse*. It is a copy — maybe a replica by the Master's hand. I cannot pass judgment on these matters. Even the Dresden picture is a poor one, done during one of the most desperate periods of the Master's life — around the time he was forced into bankruptcy and his house sold over his head. The reason why I (a Rembrandt enthusiast) chose to present these poor pictures here is the handling of the hands.

Our great Master actually cheated in this instance. He did not want to appear left-handed. So he tampered with the mirror-image of his left arm and hand which most likely held the palette. He put a pencil into this hand as if it were a right hand drawing in some small book. In the Dresden portrait he made an attempt to add another hand acceptable as a "left" hand, holding the sketch book. It would be a mirror-image of his right hand when *not* painting — before his next strokes with the brush. In the San Francisco picture parts of the fingers are cut away. They must have offended the copyist.

I have already mentioned the self-portrait in which Rembrandt sort of imitated the composition in a Raphael portrait (see Fig. 31). Rembrandt shows himself resting his left arm (his "right"-looking arm) on a parapet (Fig. 68) and with a somewhat jaunty headgear of happier days. This type of "solution" of the left hand problem is, of course, nothing new. As I have already discussed, Dürer *senior*, in his Albertina portrait-drawing, offered the same solution some 150 years earlier. No one (as far as I can tell) has ever improved it. Here are some random examples.

Fig. 66

Fig. 67

Fig. 68

Fig. 69

Fig. 70

Fig. 71

54

Fig. 72

Fig. 73

Fig. 74

First, a fine self-portrait by Nicolas Poussin (Fig. 69), in the Louvre. We see a hand and arm which look as if they were a right hand and arm, while what we see is in fact the transferred mirror-image of the artist's left. A left hand usually holds a palette. This, of course, is omitted. What looks like a right hand is holding onto something (a block of paper?).

There is quite a distance from Poussin both in space and time to the American artist Thomas H. Benton. His self-portrait (Fig. 70) painted in 1910 is quite realistic in showing how awkward things can become if the angle between subject, canvas and mirror are varied for some reason. We see that the artist had to turn his head toward the right and his eyes to the extreme left. (In the picture it looks the opposite — but we have to get used to this if we really want to study self-portraits.) He used the good old Dürer *senior* trick to portray his left arm. In this case what the artist holds in his hand is a hat. Neither Poussin nor Benton took up the challenge of the right hand.

Next I want to discuss two self-portraits by Gianlorenzo Bernini (Figs. 71 and 72) which are in the Pitti Palace in Florence. One of these presents the artist as a young man; the other, in his older years. There is much an ophthalmologist can see in these paintings. The light in both instances came from the artist's left side, illuminating the left half of his face. He was turning his head toward his left shoulder so that he saw more of the right half of his face in the mirror. He was young, so he could get quite close to the canvas and to the mirror (with his presumably dominant right eye even closer than with the left) and his gaze turned toward his right. Later he painted himself again as a middle-aged person. There are some differences between the two portraits which I guess only an ophthalmologist is likely to notice. In his younger years, Bernini could get quite close to a mirror and to his mirror-image, thus, his face covers much of the canvas. In the portrait done in his later years his head occupies less than half of the height of the canvas, suggesting that the artist had to step back from the mirror to see himself in sharp focus. He had become presbyopic (farsighted in the strictest sense of the word) and not only did he need to stand farther from the mirror, he also had to turn his head in the opposite direction so that the dominant right eye got still farther from the mirror than the other eye. (His gaze had to turn accordingly.) All this in order to secure the best possible focus with the right eye.

But let me return to Rembrandt. The next example (Fig. 73) is his famous self-portrait in the Frick Collection dated 1658. Again we can actually "see" that while he "did" the painting the light was coming from his (the artist's) left side. Obviously, what appeared best illuminated to him was the mirror-image of the left side of his face. From now on I shall take all of this for granted.

Next we come to another one of Rembrandt's few three-quarter-length or full-length self-portraits which also is one of the few rare ones in which both hands are symmetrically presented. Both hands are idle. This great Vienna three-quarter portrait (Fig. 74, dated 1652) and one of his rare full-length drawings (Fig. 75) also show both hands resting — not the

Fig. 75

way Rembrandt really saw them while working (transferring his mirror-image). Even at the pinnacle of his career our great Master would not face himself as an apparent left-hander. There was obviously no need to use a palette while he was doing the drawing, so his left hand *was* idle and he could draw it "true to life." Taken with a grain of salt, the left hand's mirror-image in the Vienna portrait could also be called "true to life."

But what about the right hand's mirror-images? No indication of a drawing hand in either instance. Rembrandt somehow managed to handle the situation by producing acceptable "pendants" to the mirror-images of his *left* hand. In the Vienna portrait the hands are sketchy anyway — details just indicated. In the Frick Collection self-portrait the Master painted one idle hand, the mirror-image of the *left* hand. (It looks like an idly resting hand.) He might have discarded the palette *while* he was sketching this hand with his right hand. The other hand is once more a quasi mirror-image of the left hand's painted image. And it is still a rather poorly painted hand. (He finally painted a maalstock into the hand's image, thus giving it greater left-hand authenticity.) Even the shadow cast by the maalstock over the hand has not been forgotten. In spite of these difficulties it is all just a marvel. Keen observer as he was, he knew it but unlike Leonardo, he never put in writing that the things that are farther from the source of light present themselves to the eye in darker tones and should be so represented on the canvas. And what subtle details! Observe the sleeves. See on the left side the play of light on the fine folds (especially over the lower arm). They connect hand and arm to the rest of the body. And then look at the other side. Note the lack of detail in the darker material that covers the arm.

There is another detail that is common to these two Rembrandt self-portraits. Doing them the artist must have looked directly at his own mirror-image, thus, in the paintings, he looks straight ahead but not at us. His gaze is piercing through us. Also (as enlarged detail views of the picture testify) more of the inside white of the left eye (of the mirror-image of the left eye) is visible. The right eye must have been his fixating eye.

It is said that the Master never did much reading, but that in his good years he had quite a respectable art collection. Did he know about Dürer *senior's* solution? Did he know about Dürer *junior's* experimentings? With the Frick Collection's self-portrait dating from 1658, we know that Rembrandt still had another eight years to live. He still did a number of self-portraits, two among them quite well known. They show an old man with the tools of his trade in hand. He must have been quite tired of and embarrassed by his circumlocutions of many decades. There is little emphasis on the hands or the tools. And he finally stopped bothering about hands. In the self-portraits of his later years the hands, if. at all indicated, add little to the picture's message.

Fig. 76 *Fig.* 77

The "Laughing Self-Portrait"—
Is it a Self-Portrait?

One cannot write about Rembrandt's self-portraits without mentioning the one that is probably best known among them — the famed "Laughing Self-Portrait," in Cologne, West Germany (Fig. 76). I have known of it ever since I read (nearly sixty years ago) the first of many books on Rembrandt, a small volume by the Belgian poet, Emile Verhaeren. In Gasser's selection of self-portraits (which depicts only one single example from the work of any artist) this self-portrait is *the* choice. We also meet it in Trevor-Roper's book. Lecturers, books, seminars dealing with Rembrandt, even conversations with artist friends, keep this portrait in the focus of general attention. (Gasser uses the word "enigma" reporting on some of its features.) Not unlike the "Mona Lisa" it has some mysterious public appeal — one is "smiling," the other "laughing." Usually it is described as "that great reckoning with himself" of an old, sad, disappointed and lonely man. But it is — we are then reassured — not his last statement. There is one later picture (Fig. 77) probably done in 1669, the year the Master died. This last picture of himself is much more formal, much more serene, much more traditional, much more "in line" with earlier self images. The last picture shows — we are told — that before he died he finally had made peace with himself. But this is not our "thing" to pursue. I better limit myself to visual physiology. What my eye-doctor's eye will notice is that the Cologne portrait is the only one among the seventy-odd paintings which the artist did of himself in which *the light is not coming from the left.* This is what is so strange, so unique about it. The unusual direction of the light (coming from the right side) is accurately, even forcefully, indicated by a rather broad strip of material which (in Gasser's words) "catches the strongest light in the picture." (Illumination of some detail of garment — a shawl, a collar — *from the left* is a common feature of dozens of both portraits and self-portraits by Rembrandt.) This most unusual feature — illumination coming from the right — repeats itself in the distribution of light over the face. It is the side of the face nearer the *right* edge of the canvas which in this unique case is better illuminated. In a good and sufficiently large color-reproduction (as in the Gasser volume) we can almost see the extra amount of luminous pigment the artist had applied to the side of the nose and to the side of the forehead nearer the right edge of the canvas. In all other painted self-portraits (there is no exception) or in most painted portraits (here there are some exceptions) the light comes from the artist's left.

Why did he do it? This is the mystery. I know an amateur should not say such things (and I have no way to study the history of the paintings) but *I doubt it altogether that this is a self-portrait of the artist.* And if this "hunch" is correct then the "mystery" is solved. Rembrandt did paint some portraits (mostly story-telling pictures with *ambiance*) in which illumination was coming from the right. But in these cases he indicated the uncommon direction of the source of light — a window on the right, a fireplace, etc.

Among the many books I have on Rembrandt there is an old compilation of the painted *oeuvre* edited by W.R. Valentino. In this book the "Laughing Self-Portrait" and the last self-portrait happen to appear on the same page. Comparing the two I can hardly believe that they are (even could be) the same person. (Some specialist in physiognomy should investigate the problem.)

One can see the vague outline of a maalstock in the lower left quadrant of the picture-space of our "enigma" portrait and then there is that unexplained profile on the extreme left of the canvas (near the top). For some reason this detail reminds me of another profile — the virtuous brother of the prodigal son in that great painting of Rembrandt's declining years, "The Return of the Prodigal Son" (in the Hermitage). Was the "Laughing Self-Portrait," by any chance, a sketch for some other projected painting which at that time occupied the artist's mind?

Dürer Once Again

Having spent all these beautiful hours in the company of two masters of the art of self-portraiture, Dürer and Rembrandt, it is difficult for me to decide how and with what examples to continue. I also have a hard time placing any name ahead of Rembrandt's of whom I like to paraphrase the words the Bible chose about Moses: there never came in Israel one like him. But Dürer was born well over one hundred years before Rembrandt. There is moreover sufficient intrinsic evidence in the pictorial record of the 15th century to credit Dürer with the discovery of mirrored space, more significantly, the *concept* of a mirror-space.

Leafing through Gasser's volume on self-portraits we note that the order in which the individual artists are presented is based on the year of birth (as good a basis, I think, as any). There are six names (six pictures) that precede Dürer's. One of them is a small medallion, not a painting (and here not relevant). The first, the oldest of the other five examples, is a detail of one of the Apostles in that famous painting called "The Tribute Money" by Tommaso Di Ser Giovanni, called Massaccio, in the church Sta. Maria del Carmine, in Florence. It is supposedly a self-portrait of the artist. I still remember the awe with which I entered that famous chapel over forty years ago well prepared and anticipating the sight of one of the originative masterpieces of the early Renaissance. (Massaccio died young, in 1428, just a few years before Alberti published his treatise and Van Eyck painted the "Arnolfini.") The last of the five of Gasser's examples (still just a detail) is the picture of one of the characters on the "Isenheim" altar in Colmar, in the Alsace. It is said to be a self-portrait of the artist, Matis Grünewald.

Neither of the examples is a "sit-in" portrait, a self-portrait *sensu strictiori*, presented *as such*. In all five examples the "self" is partly stolen into the composition. The artist presented himself as one of the figures in space — the picture's space. The three Dürer self-portrait paintings (Gasser chose the one now in the Prado) are really the first ones avowedly such — the first *real* self-portraits, the first portraits of a "self" to fill a canvas, the first transferred images of a mirror-image. The self-portrait of the Gasser selection dates a few years after Dürer had done those two pen-and-ink drawings (see Figs. 53 and 54) which represent his epoch-making contribution, his discovery of the space behind the "looking glass." These two drawings make sense only (I repeat: only) if one assumes that there was a mirror between the two: the "felt self" and the "seen self," the latter in a space impenetrable except in imagination or by the tools of mathematical logic. It should be remembered that both of these methods were successfully tried by Lewis Carroll (Alice's creator), and Charles Dodgson (the logician), and the beauty of it all is that these two people happened to be the same person.

By the time Rembrandt appeared on the scene, the mirror-image had become an established concept and even the manipulations, the tamperings with it have become quite familiar. By the time he was born, the basic discoveries pertinent to the art of Western (i.e., Western-European) picture-making had all been made. Linear perspective, light geometry, *chiaroscuro*, oil for tempera, the principles and the tools of print-making and — last but not least — the concept of mirrored space were all here ready to bring an "autobiography without words" to which, so far, no match has been created. It is not simply the vastness of the material. It is also the ultimate mastery of the presentation. So our eyes are getting biased and we forget Dürer, the 13-year-old prodigy with his drawing hand "out of the picture" and the 22-year-old young man who discovered the space "behind the looking glass" — a space that answers to rules of its own. So the order must be: Dürer first. Rembrandt, of course, also was a very great human being and our love and admiration can all be his. (But here I think I should stop. Talking about such things is truly not within the ophthalmologist's domain.) And we still have to add another point to Dürer's score. He avoided the appearance of left-handedness but never actually tampered with the record — his own retinal image — as Rembrandt sometimes did (although always half-heartedly). Of course, the whole issue lost much of its sting as time went on.

Fig. 78

Random Notes on Some 19th Century Self-Portraits

Self-portraits occupy considerable space in the *oeuvre* of 19th century artists. After the invention of photography, artists occasionally used a photograph of themselves as the basis of design. We cannot, therefore, always tell whether the eye nearer, say, the left border of the picture canvas is the mirror-image of the artist's eye (as it is in the case of a genuine self-portrait), or, perchance, a transferred photograph of his right eye. (I know of at least one self-portrait by Paul Gauguin which quite obviously was based on a photograph.) Children of a century of greater artistic freedom, they tried to paint what they actually saw — paying no attention to apparent left-handedness. A self-portrait by Cézanne and one by Van Gogh (Figs. 78 and 79) are good examples. Looking into the mirror, each of them saw not only himself (part of himself) but also a part of the back-side of the canvas to the front-side of which he was applying daubs of pigments with his working hand — his right hand. As it happens the drawing (right) hand is covered up by the canvas (it is somewhat outside the mirrored space) and neither of the artists felt the need of dragging it in. They both saved themselves some trouble. They both did include their left hands into their compositions (also the palettes) the way they actually saw them. That they looked like right hands did not bother them anymore. No heroics, but also nothing spectacular.

Fig. 79

Fig. 80

Fig. 81

The heroics were left for an actually not very heroic-looking artist Max Liebermann (see his self-portrait — Fig. 58) and the "crazy" Hungarian, Csontváry (see his self-portrait, Fig. 59, which is unusual in composition). The heroic attempt of these two artists was, as we should remember: to present both hands "true to life," and both of them within the mirrored space. That they appeared to be left-handers was seemingly of no concern.

My next item (next, by a multiplicity of associations) is a self-portrait drawing by a Russian artist, Pavel Tchelitchew (Fig. 80). The artist reproduced (and quite faithfully) how he saw himself sitting on the floor — feet stretched out toward the mirror, thus very much closer to the mirror than his head. ("Funny" is, I guess, the best way of characterizing the piece.) The feet are tremendous, especially one of them. The head and the drawing hand appear to be too small, especially in relation to the feet. Optically all this is correct and young Dürer knew it already. (As we have already discussed, this is what made the images of his hands so big.) The artist did the drawing with his right hand and, not unlike Dürer, succeeded in perpetuating a mirror-image (more accurately: the memory-image of a mirror-image) of the working right hand just ready to engage in the drawing of a line. Unlike Dürer, he did not discard the drawing utensil. Our artist certainly did nothing to improve on his appearance (that ridiculous foot and that ridiculous toe!), and he also did not mind looking left-handed. He just drew what he saw of his right hand a moment earlier — in negative time! (It seems, we must conclude, that even truth can be funny.) The clever and sophisticated artist used the mirror-image of a large sheet of drawing paper to camouflage the relation of his hand (the drawing hand) to the rest of the body. (The great Dürer, too, failed on this point. Remember the disembodied hand in Fig. 54.) And even so, Tchelitchew's rendering of his drawing right hand is of poor quality, especially if one compares it with the image of the other hand.

I shall continue here with another Russian: Marc Chagall. His "Self-Portrait with Seven Fingers" (Fig. 81) is anything but pleasing to the eye. It derives from the artist's cubist period. We need to study it the way we study a picture puzzle in order to decipher what it represents. After a while I find a palette (near the lower left corner of the picture canvas) held by a right-looking left hand with thumb and four fingers. The other hand which is nearer to the right border of the canvas is obviously the left-looking image of the artist's working right hand — it could not be uglier. The hand points at a canvas and easel. The artist is obviously working on a typical Chagall village theme.

Approaching such a picture with classical prejudice we could call the picture false, impossible, surrealistic. Not even Liebermann or Csontváry were able to get both hands and the picture all into one composition. Once we have given into cubist nonperspective our appreciation changes: "ugly" becomes "attractive" and "impossible" becomes "interesting."

"Las Meninas"

And now we come to one of the seven wonders of the art world of portraiture and of self-portraiture, *"Las Meninas"* by Diego Rodriguez de Silva y Velázquez (Fig. 82a) in the Prado Museum in Madrid. It is one of the earliest (1656) "surrealist" paintings — surrealistic on several counts. The artist must have been standing somewhere in the position where we, the spectators, are. Not otherwise could he be looking at the young princess in order to paint her with her *entourage,* and two servants(?) all in a rather cramped room, the depth of which is in a masterful and sophisticated manner indicated by an open door in the back and a man (let me call him a courtier) occupying most of the door space. The door is just about as tall as the courtier. Now, as psychology textbooks will emphasize, the size of a person is one of the best indicators of seen distance. Thus we "know" how far away the open door and the back wall are — including the framed mirror hanging on the wall just to the left of the open door. Having the size of the courtier as basis, no stereopsis is needed to "know" the distance. While the Master was painting, the King (Philip of Spain) and the Queen must have been standing and watching him working — somewhere behind his back. Obviously the artist wanted to let *us,* the people, know that *they,* the royal couple, were present, so he painted their image in the mirror on the back wall of the room. The optics and the perspective are rather complex. As I just said the open door and the courtier's silhouette tell us how far back the mirror is. The images of the King and Queen, in the mirror, are maybe the size of the courtier. They were seen by the artist "behind" the mirror — as far behind the mirror as they were actually standing in front of it.

Fig. 82a

Fig. 82b

So far, so good. It is a beautiful painting. What makes the painting so unique, so remarkable, is the fact that the artist himself appears in the painting and in a position in which he could not have been while painting the young princess. We see a tremendous canvas occupying a good part of the left side of the picture-space and next to it we see the self-portrait. Why he wanted to give us the impression ("The Great Surrealist Double Hoax") that he is actually painting the King and Queen (seen by *us* in the mirror but not by him!) I never did really understand. That this is a self-portrait has never been doubted. And a great self-portrait it is. (Gasser did right by choosing it for the back of the dust jacket of his book.) But as great a draftsman as Velázquez was, he still painted his *own* hands poorly — much worse than Rembrandt did. He shows himself holding a brush in what is supposed to be his right hand, though it is the mirror-image of the left hand which usually holds the palette. (What a terrible claw!) And the other hand? No better. The details shown in Figure 82b leave us with no doubt about this.

Velázquez's trick of insinuating himself into a group portrait of important people found followers. Goya (Francisco Goya y Lucientes) was also a court-painter. Figure 83 is a formal portrait, now in the Prado, of King Carlos IV and family (painted in 1808). No need to discuss the point that the artist also could not have been in the position in which he painted himself. As in the Velázquez painting, here, too, the image of a rather large canvas occupies the extreme left of the picture-space and we see a small head sticking out from behind. It has obviously no connection with the royal family. It is a self-portrait — but it is not at all pretentious.

This arrangement must have intrigued another Spanish artist (a Spanish-American artist), the contemporary painter-satirist, Bernardo Botero. (Critics and dealers call him a "surrealist," however, I don't quite know why.) In his "Presidential Family" (Fig. 84, shown some years ago at the Museum of Modern Art), we see some imaginary Latin-American dictator with his wife, brothers and children. In the background is the artist's self-portrait — all in the style which is this painter's trademark.

Fig. 83

Fig. 84

Fig. 85

There is also another way for an artist to hide his self-portrait in a picture. A good example is seen in a painting by one of Velázquez's assistants, Juan de Pareja — "The Calling of St. Matthew" (Fig. 85), in the Prado. In this *tableau* most of the faces and gazes are turned toward the key figure — Christ. However, there is one person near the left edge of the canvas who is not looking at the chief character in the scenario. He is looking at us. Our artist obviously painted himself into the picture-space while looking into a mirror. I might mention, by the way, that one of the characters in the painting, the elderly man with pen and paper (one of the two who seem to be writing) has a pair of spectacles perched on his nose. He too looks at Christ — not at his paper. I guess the painter did not realize that reading-glasses are taken off when one is not reading. (Bifocals were not yet invented.) El Greco's "Grand Inquisitor" (see Fig. 20) (painted around 1600) must have been one of the first persons who (in a way documented by his portrait) habitually wore glasses to see — even when sitting for formal portraits. (Was he a myope who took his glasses off when he read? Who knows!)

I might mention that in Velázquez's "Breda" (see Fig. 100a) one can also spot a character who looks at us rather than the "event." Is it perchance a self-portrait of Velázquez?

The Goya and the Botero pictures are self-portraits of minor interest. The association that brought them to mind is obvious. Their esthetic merits or demerits are outside our jurisdiction. It is a much more complex train of associations that leads from the Velázquez to three very different and quite interesting self-portraits.

First, let me start with Edouard Manet. One of his self-portraits is in a private collection in New York and its owner loaned it to the Metropolitan Museum on several occasions for the benefit of all of us who appreciate Manet's art. I note with pleasure that Gasser has chosen it to represent Manet in his book (Fig. 86).

As Gasser points out, Manet liked to look like a dandy — hat, neck-tie

Fig. 86

Fig. 87

with pin, colorful jacket — all *comme-il-faut*. He was seemingly all dressed up for a formal portrait. An excellent observer and accurate reporter, he registered the direction of the light. (It was coming from the left.) And he also registered the dominance of his right eye. (More of the inside white of the mirror-image of the left eye is visible.) There was only one thing wrong — those hands. Manet would not (maybe could not) paint what he did not see, and what he saw of his hands in the mirror was in constant conflict with what he would have liked to put on the canvas. Oh, that annoying Jack-in-the-box type right hand — now inside, now outside the mirrored space while the real right hand tried to do an honest job. Manet was not one like Velázquez — ready to bring a false but right-looking hand into the picture-space. And he was not like Dürer, ready to take up the great challenge — the right hand of the self-portraitist as seen in a mirror. Manet was not really concerned about looking left-handed. But he could not put into the picture-space what he stopped seeing the very moment he stroked his brush against the canvas to perpetuate it. In the end he must have lost his nerve. He must have fallen into a rage. I vaguely remember some Gothic story about a man who sends a bullet into the mirror or slashes his portrait with a knife (I don't remember which) to kill some *Doppelgänger*. Manet must have felt like that. He certainly massacred (massacred is the word!) the painted image of his painting right hand. Velázquez's false right hand is just poor, while Manet's "left"-looking honest right hand is, as a picture, a catastrophe. But it is a great human document.

Second, I will show a picture by the American painter James McNeill Whistler, in the Chicago Art Institute (Fig. 87). The title of the painting, "The Artist in his Studio," brings back old memories. It is a self-portrait. It faithfully shows how an artist sees himself in a mirror — the left hand's "right"-looking image holds a big palette. (The left arm must have been closer to the mirror; obviously the artist did not stand parallel to the mirror.) The right hand's "left"-looking mirror-image (a smaller hand, farther from the mirror's plane) holds the brush. It is an extremely poorly painted hand, this hand. (Forgive the expression — a *Schmier*). We have gotten used to this by now. But where is the artist? *Is the artist in his studio?* It looks as if by some eerie, uncanny manner the artist's mirror-image would have freed itself from the mirror to be in the same room with those two ladies, *et cetera*, behind him. Behind whom?

The picture, "Rembrandt in his Studio," mentioned earlier, can only make sense if we can assume that the picture presents a model *and* an artist, Rembrandt, in the same room — both seen by another, a second artist. Velázquez's self-portrait would also make some sense under a similar assumption. Here, too, the presence of another artist is at least thinkable. This *other* artist would be occupying *our* place as we stand in front of all those personages of *"Las Meninas."* That *other* artist could have actually "seen" *all* we see — all of the *"Las Meninas"* ensemble as presented, all, including an artist (who could be Velázquez), the latter oddly hiding behind a colossal canvas. We must, of course, realize that in neither of these cases would we *technically* deal with self-portraits and a

Fig. 88

mirror would be no part of the outlay. But in the case of a self-portrait a mirror is obligatory and, according to our definition, the image presented must actually be *the* mirror-image. But how about Whistler's painting? It is a mirror-image. Is the mirror-image of the artist part of a mirror-image of his studio? Are those two female forms mirror-images? And that old-time tile stove? Is it still in the mirror's space? How could a mirror include all this? That Whistler self-portrait is certainly "surrealistic." It is in fact surreal. Eerie, as I said, and uncanny. A kind of Pygmalion's artwork that came to life. The picture is beyond rationalization. There is no arrangement even thinkable in which an artist could see himself in a mirror which mirrors all the *ambiance* presented, especially the stove we see next to the left border of the canvas, while the artist is actually turning away from all that surround. To make things even worse he turns his face toward us, where by necessity there was a mirror — *the* mirror — while he portrayed himself. But who is "he"? Is it the artist? Impossible. Is it the mirror-image? Also impossible. There is no solution. The Whistler self-portrait is "absurdistic" (if there is such a word), not surrealistic. Dali beyond Dali. All this is not a judgment on esthetic qualities or on surrealism as pertaining to art. The fact is that it is its surreal, even absurd character which makes the picture memorable — not its painterly qualities.

The third picture brought back to memory by the Velázquez painting is one called "Family Group," by Lovis Corinth (Fig. 88). At first glance there could hardly be two pictures as different as these two — one by a 17th century Spaniard, a royal court-painter with a refined brush, the other by a Prussian of the turn of the century, a realist-expressionist, one who rather roughly, gracelessly applied the pigment. Corinth died in 1925. I well remember a comprehensive exhibit of his work that year in the *Kunsthalle* of Kiel, a town in northern Germany where I happened to be a medical student. But at the second look it turns out that in composition — perhaps it could be called topology — the two are closely related. The big foreground figures of *"Las Meninas"* are here replaced by Corinth's wife and children. Like the former these also fill a great part of the canvas. They are presented as if seen by us, the spectators, as they were seen (*must have been seen*) by the artist *while* he painted the group. *Mutatis mutandis*, all this also applies to the Velázquez canvas. The self-portrait was obviously *added* later in both instances — the artist seeing himself in a mirror which is not presented.

There are some minor differences in topology: Velázquez insinuated himself into the upper region of the canvas, far from the royal presence. Corinth placed himself into the key-position of the canvas, showing himself as the guardian of a family, with an outstretched arm above the woman's head. He saw no reason, obviously, to change the apparent left handedness of his mirror-image.

The Corinth painting is not "nice" (if we look at it as a painted surface) and the composition is graceless, lopsided. The bulk of the man on the right side is ill-balanced by the figure on the left — a 4-year-old boy standing on a kind of coffee table (a somewhat strange arrangement, in order to balance the two sides, and not quite successfully).

After having once more studied the Whistler self-portrait I also took another look at the Corinth. And then I was not quite so sure. It seemed possible that the whole family was sitting *next* to the artist and that he painted *all of them* as seen by him in some large mirror; in any event, large enough to encompass all that is seen in the painting — the painter *and* his family. That the painter's image is a mirror-image needs no further thought. His brush-holding right hand's image is almost at the right border of the canvas. That trouble-maker (in reality, his creative hand!) is almost pushed off the canvas. It is shown in a painting pose. (Corinth was obviously not at ease doing it.) The image of the left hand (it is holding the palette) is more detailed, more conspicuous, and higher in the picture-space than usual for a self-portrait's left hand — it is the wing of the guardian angel of the family.

There are some added problems: If my last look should turn out to be the correct one, then the inevitable redistribution of right and left in the picture-space will hold for all of the characters — not only the artist. In this case it is the mother's right arm that holds the baby and it is the boy's right hand that rests on his mother's shoulder. I am sure that there are some clues. (For example, there is a ring on the third finger of what would be the "real" left hand if the latter surmise is the correct one. And by chance a photograph might turn up that would tell which hand wore the ring.)

This picture was chosen by Gasser for his selection and I am sure I have read his annotations several times. Having not been alerted, I previously missed a sentence that should settle the question. I quote:

> His wife relates in her memoirs how the whole family posed,
> just as they appear in the picture, in front of a mirror with the
> exact dimension of the canvas.

What we see then must be the mirror-portrait of the whole Corinth family. The association with *"Las Meninas"* led me in a false direction. Not that this would make me any happier. On the contrary. And I start looking for faults, for defects, for contradictory clues. It is a self-portrait's burden as well as distinction to exist in *negative* space. And this negative space is full of surprises. Velázquez did not know about them. At his time, "space" was still space. So he could blithely leave the mirror out of consideration. Nobody, including the artist, saw anything absurd in his figure being imbedded into the *"Las Meninas"* space. (And everybody took it for granted that an arm and a hand, which in the picture appear nearer to its left border, are the right arm and the right hand for both, the princess in *premier plan* and the artist in the background.) The same did not hold for Whistler's time — for Whistler placed an eerie though honest self-portrait into a milieu he did not care to define. I guess, he did not read E.T.A. Hoffmann, or Lewis Carroll. (Botero just pulls a prank. He does not want to be taken seriously.) In any event according to Mme. Corinth's memoirs, the Corinth self-plus-family-portrait was all done from negative space. (It seems other such self-plus-portraits should be studied with an "eye" for the problem. There must be other such portraits in existence.)

Velázquez's famed self-portrait adorns the back cover of Gasser's selection. A fine choice. Even with the faked and poorly done brush-yielding hand it is a great self-portrait and a part of one of the timeless masterpieces of art. What we will be intrigued with is how editor Gasser made his choice for the front cover — a pleasant but comparatively minor work, a self-portrait from the younger years of the "noted" British painter, Reynolds (later Sir Joshua Reynolds, President of the Royal Academy). From the notes that accompany the portrait (Fig. 89) we learn that this artist "presents himself here with his *left* hand shading his eyes and his *right* hand grasping brush, palette and maalstock — an odd striking pose." (Italics mine.) And we are also told that "this highly original gesture was obviously meant to conceal some embarrassment."

The embarrassment is really mine. (Oh, that ghost of the *Dürer-Blick* controversy.) I am the one who is embarrassed to tell a professional art critic that he is in error — but there is no other word for it.

Too bad I have to repeat all this. *A self-portrait is the artist's mirror-image transferred by him upon a picture surface.* With no exception, *the eye, the hand nearer the right border of the picture surface is the image of the artist's right* — whatever else is said and whatever doctoring the artist might have done to confuse us. Reynolds held his palette in his left hand and had no difficulty transferring what he saw and how he saw it upon his canvas — all, of course, done with his (let me add, invisible) right hand. But this is easy. The challenge is to imagine the right hand as the painting hand. Young Dürer's bravado, Edouard Manet's madness were not for our Reynolds. His solution is as good as anyone's (Frans Hals' included) and certainly many are worse than his: an unobtrusive, well-drawn hand, a "left"-looking hand that is out of the way. It shades the eyes and produces a lovely pattern of a cast shadow across the face. And the more I look at the picture on Gasser's cover, the more I like it. It is a fine, human (I repeat, unobtrusive) "solution" of the right-hand problem. I might have chosen the Dürer or the Manet for the cover. But I think Gasser made a very wise choice.

I will now, with his kind permission, interpolate a self-portrait by a young, left-handed artist, Robert E. Bowen, Jr. Mr. Bowen is a friend and has been a patient of mine for quite some time. His case is one of the two cases described in my book, *On Writing, Reading and Dyslexia* (1973), in the chapter on left-handedness. He and a friend of his make their livings as commercial artists which means that much of their art-work includes letters, words, some text. They both write with their left hands, but naturally, they both learned (or, rather, had to learn) to write and read our way — from left to right — since that is the only way for them to communicate with us, the right-handed majority. But painting is different. Once I asked them to make a poster from the words "NEW YORK WORLD'S FAIR." Both told me that once they had finished the design with text included in the usual left to right pattern, it was easier for them to do the filling-in, the shading, the coloring brush-work from right to left, a manner more natural to them.

Mr. Bowen's "Self-Portrait as a Yacht Designer" (Fig. 90) is quite

Fig. 90

remarkable (and I am not only referring to its artistic merits). The artist presents (in fact, declares) himself a left-hander and quite assertively so. His left-handedness is, for me, the actual message of the picture. Of course, self-portraits are tricky. We are never safe from surprises. So, if we come to analyze it we find that the artist had to put a brush into his really inactive hand in order to make its mirror-image appear as an active left hand. He did the painting with the left hand, the mirror-image of which looks like a right hand. (Oh, the ghost of Dürer!) So the role of the active left hand has to be actually de-emphasized to make it appear as the inactive hand and still keep within the mirrored space. Mr. Bowen did well, unusually well, in accomplishing both — at least as well as young Reynolds did. I had to look a second time even to find that other hand since it was so successfully put out of the way, that inactive-looking hand. Strange, as repetitive as it may sound, it is the mirror-image of the artist's active left hand that is now almost hidden somewhere at the bottom of the picture-space. The amazing thing — the mystery of it all — is that in spite of all this, the message of the painting still came through.

Fig. 89

Fig. 92

Fig. 93

Fig. 91

An Epilogue on Buttons and Buttonholes and Photo-Portraits of Self

Let me now (before closing this seemingly never-ending chapter) once more return to the German collection of *Five Hundred Self-Portraits.* Here we see a different Manet (Fig. 91) — a fine work of art, also an example of the artist's integrity. He did not present anything he did not see. The editor's notes which accompany the portrait refer to Manet as "the founder of the new impressionism" which, to a degree, is true. What Manet and impressionism had in common was the free and open handling of brush-strokes — easily recognized even in the black-and-white reproduction. (By the way, they clearly show that the artist was right-handed.) What prompted me to turn added attention to this particular painting is a seemingly unimportant detail of portraiture. I am referring to the arrangement of *buttons* and *buttonholes* in contemporary Western male apparel.

I don't know too much about sartorial history, but by now we all take certain arrangements for granted. We (I mean men) wear the buttons of our coats fastened to the right breastpiece while buttonholes are cut into the left one. This arrangement necessarily makes the left lapel fold over the right one. We also take it for granted that the slit in men's trousers, shorts, underwear is always covered with a fold from the left. The reasons for this are obvious. They have to do with right-handedness and that "little difference" between the male and female anatomies. Any man can easily verify this. Take the Minkowski photo-portrait (Fig. 92). It tells us that the buttonholes were cut into the left breastpiece of his coat. (The two buttons nearer the left arm are only for decoration.) The Hurwitz photo-portrait (Fig. 93) shows the coat already buttoned. A part of one of the buttonholes is still visible. It was obviously also cut into the left breastpiece. In both of these photo-portraits the right side of the face is illuminated. The source of the light was obviously on these subject's right side while these photo-graphs were taken. But this is not obligatory. The photo-portrait of Hilbert (Fig. 94) presents an elderly gentleman sitting at a desk. For reading or writing he uses a light coming from his left. This will leave the right half of the face in the dark. (Note the hands emerging from an almost Rembrandtesque undetailed background.) The Hurwitz portrait also shows clearly that it is the left lapel that crosses over the other.

Comparing the Hurwitz photo-portrait with the Manet self-portrait (see Fig. 91) will do more than words to pin down the difference. In a true

Fig. 94

Fig. 95

Fig. 96

self-portrait (a transferred mirror-image) it is the mirror-image of the left lapel (the lapel nearer the left border of the canvas) which seems to cross over the other. No question: Manet painted what he saw.

I have already mentioned another asymmetric feature of coats: the breastpocket on the left side. (Occasionally suits, vests might have two breastpockets, but never do we encounter just *one* on the *right side*.)

If we open this German book of self-portraits to page 419 we cannot help also looking at the painting on page 418. We cannot help comparing this portrait of the Swiss-German painter Arnold Böcklin with the Manet self-portrait. The Böcklin self-portrait is a beautiful piece (Fig. 95) — a successful artist, a handsome man. But the painting certainly does not represent what he must have seen looking into a mirror. The painting reminds me of Anthonis Mor whose self-portrait I discussed earlier in this chapter (see Fig. 50). I was then led to the conclusion that he might have used a dummy while finishing his self-portrait. Böcklin's self-portrait is also the work of a master-artist but again what we see on the canvas could not possibly have been what he saw in the mirror. He obviously did not need a dummy; he must have used a photograph of himself. The Manet portrait is a genuine *bona fide* self-portrait — the transferred image of the image of the "self" he saw in the mirror. The Böcklin picture is a pseudo-self-portrait. Obviously, the painter did not notice that (as "culprits" often do) he had left some clues behind. Buttonholes, buttons, lapels, vest-pockets give away that the artist did not look at his "self" in a mirror but at a photograph of himself. (It is of some interest that the editor uses phrases like "realistic" and "almost photographic fidelity" in the evaluation of the portrait.) Incidentally, the distribution of the light indicates that while his photograph was taken, the source of the light must have been to his (the artist's) left — just what we would expect to find in an artist's studio. This will leave the right half of the artist's face in the dark. And as we can expect in the Böcklin picture (let me call it a "photo-self-portrait") the right half of the artist's face is in the dark. This, of course, is not mandatory. After all, a photographer *could* have illuminated the other half of the painter's face. But this is less probable. So, whenever I see a "self-portrait" in which the half of the face nearer to the left border of the canvas is in the dark, I suspect that a photograph has been used as an intermediary. Cézanne's self-portrait in a museum in Bern (Fig. 96) is a good example. Usually the only accurate and revealing sartorial clue is the position of the breastpocket which (as I have already pointed out) both men's and women's coats have on the left side (or on both sides, never just on the right side). Thus, in a genuine mirror-image self-portrait, the breastpocket will be (if shown at all) depicted nearer to the left border of the picture-space. Liebermann's second "Cigarette" self-portrait (see Fig. 56) does in fact show this feature, and so does a self-portrait by the noted 19th century Pennsylvanian, Thomas Eakins, in a painting which has no other clue to tell. In the Böcklin self-portrait we have to look carefully, but we will finally discern that there is a fine and not very conspicuous line and a fine chain exactly in the place where we would anticipate it in a photograph.

4 RIGHT AND LEFT IN PICTORIAL ART

Fig. 97

Fig. 98

In this chapter I shall discuss some problems of direction, specifically of right and left, in the picture-space. We will not be too far amiss with the generalization that Western culture (Greco-Roman-European civilization, including the Russian) for many centuries has been to a very considerable degree based on a system of writing that moves from left to right. Writing was always done with the right hand (left-handers were a curiosity even in Biblical times) and at first it most likely ran from right to left. Etruscan was and Arabic and Hebrew still are written from right to left. Chinese and Japanese writing also prefer the right-to-left direction. The Egyptians and the early Greeks did their writing in both directions. The Ten Commandments were not written down in traditional ways. They were chiseled on stone from right to left; hammer in the right hand, chisel in the left. But ever since the Greeks made their momentous, rational and final choice, all Occidental writing has been done in the more practical way: from left to right. The direction of writing settles the direction of reading (it is *not* the other way around!) and this influences the direction of gaze. Casting one's gaze from left to right becomes with us "second nature." (But only second nature: a "conditioned" reflex.) We also read picture-sequences from left to right. (Think of the direction of the picture-sequences in comic strips.) Even over an individual, non-moving, static picture (arrangement of pigments on a flat surface) our Western eye tends to move from left to right and so will usually (I believe, inadvertently) the action represented in the picture, the story which the artist (a Western artist) had planned to tell. Pictures are not static, even statues are not. Time and direction are built into them.

The following two pictures are illustrative of this right-left versus left-right movement: one is by a Western artist, the other by an Oriental. Both depict a procession of blind people — blind leading the blind. One of them (which I have already mentioned in Chapter I) is by Pieter Bruegel, the Elder (Fig. 97). It shows a string of these unfortunates holding on to each other. All of them are moving from left to right. The man on the extreme right side of the picture has just fallen into a ditch, the next one follows "blindly." What I want to emphasize is the direction. The action in the painting runs from left to right. The other picture, "Blind Men Fording a River," a work of Hokusai, the great Japanese artist (Fig. 98), also presents a procession of blind people. They are in this case moving from right to left.

Here is another pertinent and also charming example: the growth of the uterus during the nine months of pregnancy (Fig. 99). It comes from a Japanese textbook on gynecology which I saw in the Medico-Historical Museum in Budapest some years ago. Events here also follow each other from right to left. At the extreme right we see the uterus at the time of conception. Its growth is followed in nine monthly steps from then until confinement. The sequence goes from right to left. I have never found this type of arrangement in a textbook of obstetrics written or illustrated by a Westerner.

One of the minor but for me remarkable events of recent years was an exhibit in the Metropolitan Museum in the small quarters assigned to photographs and printings. It was called: "The Great Wave: The Influence of Japanese Woodcuts on French Artists." Its organizers had the fine idea of hanging, in pairs, next to each other, a Western (French) and a Japanese piece of graphic art which in some general way expressed the same pictorial idea. (Japanese prints were greatly in vogue in Europe in the second half of the last century.) As I entered the exhibit the very first pair of pictures that caught my eye was titled "Umbrellas." The Western half of the "pair" was by Manet. It depicted a scene of the Paris *Commune* of 1870: starving people standing in line for bread on a rainy day. The design was essentially a panorama of umbrellas. The other half, the Japanese counterpart, was a print, "Samurai in the Rain," again by Hokusai. Essentially it also depicted a procession of umbrellas. The Hokusai procession went from right to left. Manet's procession headed left to right. (One, even two such coincidences are no proof, I realize, just interesting. I wonder whether even the expert organizers of that lovely exhibit noticed this particular point.)

I might add here that, as far as I can tell, the story in Chinese picture-scrolls (they are picture-sequences like our comic strips) runs from right to left. (I have never made a real study of it. My knowledge is based on inquiries in the art and antique shops of San Francisco's Chinatown.) I am sure I have never seen a comic strip in which the story would not have run from left to right.

As an example of the direction of "action-in-pictures" I want to discuss here a painting by Velázquez, "The Surrender of Breda to the

Spanish Army," in the Prado (Fig. 100a). The basic geometric structure of the painting is symmetric — a triptych. The two major figures meet in the center, face to face, each with his *entourage* behind him. But the story still is asymmetric. It *runs* in both space and time. The Dutch general is shown turning over the keys of a city to the conquering Spanish general. The action, the surrender, runs from left to right; our gaze also moves in the same direction. First we see the Dutchman. We see his profile. His body bending forward, his face, his gaze are all turned toward the right. The Spaniard occupies the right half of the picture-space where the action ends. His profile turns in the other direction. He stands erect. On the left side, the Dutchman's *entourage* is quite loosely composed — some halberds, a flag, a horse in the background. On the other side we see a tremendous horse, the general's tent and a forest of straight vertical spears, all encroaching on the horizon. The action ends here. Our gaze is stopped. Our gaze moved from left to right as the action did.

We can easily demonstrate the significance of direction in painted scenarios. All we need are slides, transparencies (not reproductions). They can be turned around *before* we project them. The picture on the screen will in this case appear right-left-transposed (let us not call it "inverted")* and might look rather strange. We might have a hard time directing our gaze from right to left to read the picture's message (Fig. 100b).

A favorite example of mine is a painting called "Adoration of the Shepherds" by Andrea Mantegna in the Metropolitan Museum (Fig. 101a). Looking at the original version, our eyes will at first meet a sleeping old man (St. Joseph). With this, a mood of tranquility and domesticity is set; a mood of peace, of serenity. "Just let him sleep," we tell ourselves as our eyes glide toward the right to reach some centrally located figures — the main event. Then our eyes turn to a group of people even farther right. The gaze of these people is directed toward the left, toward those centrally located figures, obviously the main event, toward which our gaze also rebounds. The transposed version (Fig. 101b) is almost ridiculous. Our gaze first rests on a group of little people who all look in the same direction, we don't yet know why, and finally reaches some central characters only to glide further toward some large figure dominating the event side. He is asleep, he is turned away as if he were unaware of what is happening.

*Unfortunately the term "invert" has several, not well-defined meanings. As I analyzed it in another context this causes considerable confusion and I would discourage its use for the maneuver just described. A slide-projector *inverts* the projected image; what is upper right on the slide (as we hold it in our hand) becomes lower left on the screen (as we look at it). And *vice versa*. The lens of a camera also inverts. The retinal image is inverted. We can also say that we invert a slide before we project it and that the projector re-inverts it. Not so a mirror. A mirror does not invert anything. My right eye is nearer to the right border of the mirror I am looking into, and the mirror-image of my right eye is also nearer to the right border of the mirror. And both the hand and the head of my mirror-image are on the same level as are my hand and head respectively.

Fig. 99

Fig. 100a

Fig. 100b

Fig. 101a

Fig. 101b

Fig. 102

Fig. 103

The Annunciation

In paintings depicting the Annunciation (one of the favorite subjects of Renaissance religious art) we have classic examples of this duality: symmetry of composition — direction of action. It seems it has become almost fixed by tradition (possibly by some ecclesiastic ruling) that in pictures of this event the angel Gabriel makes his announcement from the left of the picture-space. He is in this case shown as turning toward the right and facing the Virgin. His outstretched right arm is nearer to us and covers his chest. The Virgin is sitting or standing in the right half of the picture-space, accepting the message, with her face turned either toward us (the community of believers for whose edification the whole story is being told) or toward the announcer, toward the left. She usually does not act.

I have seen scores of Annunciation pictures over the years — in Munich, in the Metropolitan Museum, in the National Gallery in Washington, in the Lehman Collection. I am almost certain that whenever there is an Annunciation to be seen, the arrangement will be: Angel left, Virgin right. Essentially the Annunciation story presents just two "individuals." They are interrelated and their interrelation is expressed by that great Renaissance invention of gestures. In earlier versions they were usually both placed on the same picture-plane — a perfect subject and the happy occasion for the Renaissance artist (especially of the older vintage) to show (even to show off with his proficiency) the new science of geometric perspective (which at that time was still in its infancy). It almost looks as if the display of this skill would have been the principal *raison d'être* of the artwork. Good examples are "The Annunciation" by Domenico Veneziano in Cambridge (Fig. 102) and the one by Sandro Botticelli in the Lehman Collection (Fig. 103). They are almost symmetrical and have rather static compositions built into a picture-space with a single vanishing point. My old favorites from Munich's *Alte Pinakothek* are already somewhat more sophisticated in composition. The one by Philippo Lippi (Fig. 104) offers a spirited display of arches and

Fig. 104

Fig. 105

Fig. 107

columns. The other, by Rogier van der Weyden (Fig. 105) with a window on the left wall reminds me of the Arnolfini double-portrait by his contemporary, Jan van Eyck. "The Annunciation" by Leonardo da Vinci in the Uffizi (Fig. 106) also belongs in this group. Essentially it still is a study of perspective. But the somewhat primitive symmetry is already broken: the architectural geometric display is restricted to one row of columns in the right half of the picture-surface, the Virgin's side. In the left half of the picture, architectural details are missing. Emphasis on linear perspective is minimal. Instead we encounter several planes of recession parallel to the picture-plane. Note the row of trees at mid-distance. They are spaced so as to permit a free vista up to the distant horizon. Also, note the low horizontal structures. All this adds depth. We feel that the angel is nearer to us than even the nearest of these structures (which seem to be hedges or shrubbery.) We feel him to be almost in front of the picture. The Virgin is farther than the shrubbery which the artist has cleverly terminated so as to let us see all of the Virgin's figure. If we compare the levels of the feet of the two figures, there is no question that the level of the feet of the right figure is higher. Thus, the Virgin is farther than the angel. She is also smaller — another clue for appearing farther. Leonardo was interested in the pictorial clues of seen distance hundreds of years before visual scientists started studying it. The trees in the picture are small; they present little detail. This sets them "far." The contours of the angel-figure interrupt the contours of the shrubbery. This brings it "near."

I cannot keep on presenting further examples. There would be no end and there are exceptions. Notable among them is the "Annunciation" (Fig. 107) by Lorenzo Lotto — an unexpected, almost baroque arrangement. The picture-plane is broken and the action is "in depth." The angel is on the right and farther; he is turned toward her, and also toward us. The Virgin is on the left, nearer to us and she too looks at us. She has turned away from an agitated messenger and his awesome, perhaps even frightening news. She reacts. She is by no means passive. She talks to us. She might have preferred not to have been chosen.

Another interesting exception is an Annunciation by Andrea del Sarto, in the Pitti in Florence (Fig. 108), singled out by Wölfflin in his book, *Classic Art*. I quote from the English edition: "The angel is as beautiful as only Leonardo could have made him with all the charm of youthful ardour." (In fact, Andrea's angel reminded Wölfflin of Leonardo's "beautiful" boys.) One need not be a Freudian-depth psychologist to see that the traditional positions of the two *dramatis personae* are interchanged. Wölfflin, of course, brings an estheticist's explanation: "The angel enters from the right, and the reason for this might have been Andrea's desire to prevent the outstretched right arm covering the body — since it is only thus that the figure can be expressed with full clarity." And he even adds that "the arm is bare." It is interesting to quote another statement by Wölfflin in connection with Andrea's religious art: "The falling off in sincerity of conception." Much of the Italian Renaissance art is great but not "religious."

It was just about the same time that the Russian writer-philosopher,

Fig. 108

Fig. 106

Fig. 109

Fig. 110

Dimitri Merejkovski published his historical novel (part of a trilogy) on the life of Leonardo. It has been more than fifty years since I read this novel but I still remember the "analysis" of the strange relationship between Leonardo and some of his young and handsome pupils. (It seems that times were ready for Freud to come.)

Several Annunciation paintings by El Greco exist. One (Fig. 109) is in the Metropolitan Museum. All his Annunciations are exceptions to the left-to-right rule. But El Greco is just different. We have to take him on his own terms.

The usual (or prevalent) left-right arrangement can get reversed for some purely mechanical (and often non-intentional) reason. A good example is tapestry weaving based on a design ("cartoon"). The "right" side (i.e., the side to be displayed) will be a mirror-image of the cartoon. This has to do with the technique of tapestry-weaving on which I shall not elaborate. The same holds for any kind of picture material to be multiplied by some printing process. Figure 110 presents such a cartoon — the traditional arrangement of the Annunciation theme. The angel is presented on the left side, the Virgin on the right; the angel gives his blessing with his elevated right hand. A print based on such a cartoon (Fig. 111) renders a mirror-image. The angel now occupies the right half of the picture-space and he extends his salutations with the left hand. There can be hardly any question that the printer followed the original cartoon in every detail. Note for instance the arrangement: box, flowerpot and pitcher or the placement of the window, the left hand of the Virgin. The same will also happen if the original serves as a cartoon for some kind of needle work. A charming series of such needlework-pieces, an altar-frontal depicting the life of the Virgin, can be seen at the Cloisters in New York City. We should note that the individual pieces are arranged from left to right, as expected. The series starts with the birth of the Virgin on the left, and ends with her coronation on the extreme right. This arrangement is natural in our civilization and there might possibly also have been some ruling by proper church-authorities to hold to this arrangement. But the ruling did not possibly cover arrangements within the individual pieces of handiwork, each of them executed following some drawing or painting as its cartoon, its guide. So it became transposed during the execution. Thus, the piece which, for instance, shows the Annunciation (Fig. 112) is also a mirror-image — the angel, entering from the right, gives his salutation with the left hand. Another piece shows the Visitation of the Virgin by St. Elizabeth (Fig. 113). We will note that they are greeting each other by

Fig. 111

Fig. 113

Fig. 112

Fig. 116

Fig. 114

Fig. 115

Fig. 117

Fig. 118

shaking each other's left hand. In the Coronation piece a musician-angel plucks her harp with the left hand. Obviously the artists or designers of the time and place these pieces were made were not too concerned with this type of right-and-left transposition.

Being obsessed by this notion of direction I was set back when during a tour through Brussels' Ste. Gudule Cathedral I noticed that a series of paintings representing the Stations of the Cross were arranged in the direction right-to-left. I have since found this particular subject arranged in this particular manner in other Catholic churches. (I could, alas, not follow up with an inquiry about *why*. I am sure there is a reason.)

Next I want to show a drawing (Fig. 114) and an engraving (Fig. 115) by Bruegel. The drawing (preserved in the Hamburg *Kunsthalle*) served as a cartoon for the engraving, and was also a study for his well-known painting in the Metropolitan Museum. The drawing depicts a summertime scene and the prominent figure in it is a man on the right side, a man with a scythe. For those familiar with such scenery (as I am, having come from a small town of mostly peasants) there is something strange in this figure; he swings the scythe with his left hand. Bruegel was employed by a firm which produced engravings for the market based on such drawings. In the engraving made after this drawing, right and left of the drawing are reversed (not inverted). Thus the engraving is "right." (Note the double meaning of the word!) The man now wields the scythe with the right hand. Obviously, when Bruegel produced the drawing he knew that it was going to be turned into an engraving. He did the drawing in reverse order to make the engraving "right."

Figure 116 from the Egyptian collection of the Metropolitan Museum shows a group of warriors. All of them hold spears in their right hands and shields in their left. It is, I believe, our endowment by now to have our right hand dominant. It is not "learned" like language but (Hail Chomsky!) "inborn" like speech. This dominance manifests itself in all kinds of situations: the painter holds the palette in the left hand and draws with the right (Fig. 117). The cellist, the violinist wield the bow with their right hand and do the fingering with the left (Fig. 118).

Fig. 119

Fig. 120

Raphael Tapestries and the Right and Wrong Side of the Sistine Madonna

This should be the appropriate place to discuss some of the famous tapestries by Raphael in the Sistine Chapel* in the Vatican. These tapestries are glorious works of art. They illustrate some of the highlights in the lives of Sts. Peter and Paul. The original drawings, the cartoons by Raphael (as many as are preserved), are in the Victoria and Albert Museum in London. A section of one of the tapestries is called "The Miracle of the Fish" (Fig. 119). We should note that this figure is a photograph of a piece of tapestry, not of a cartoon. (Actually several copies exist. I saw another one in New York City, in the Cathedral of St. John the Divine.) We can see that Christ, the principal character of the story, is placed near the right border of the picture-space, facing toward the left. The action — Peter (called Simon at that time) and Andrew recognizing him — flows from left to right. The tertiary characters, some fishermen, the birds (lovely decorative elements) are situated on the extreme left. Peter's brother, Andrew, is standing up — Peter has already sunk to his knees (note the "time" element!). Finally, Jesus offers his blessing by stretching out his arm. The spectator's gaze is also directed from left to right, coming to rest in the infinity of the landscape at the upper right corner of the picture-space. Fortunately the original drawing is also preserved (although parts of it are severely mutilated). Figure 120 is a photograph of the cartoon. In the cartoon we find Christ sitting far to the left and we note that he is shown giving his blessing with the left hand. The action, the movement of the two acting figures, flows from right to left. The upper right-hand corner of the picture-space (where our gaze is

*The chapel is named for Pope Sixtus IV (della Rovere), the "sponsor" of this and several other great artists' projects that immortalize his name and reign. As a point of information: the "Sistine Madonna," also by Raphael, is named after a 5th century martyr-pope, St. Sixtus II — not after the Renaissance Pope. Wölfflin's great book abounds in such interesting details. (Of course, the *Britannica* also helps.)

Fig. 121

Fig. 123

Fig. 122

Fig. 124a

Fig. 124b

supposed to come to rest) is now occupied by a cut-off landscape. The whole thing is a kind of a side-show and those tertiary characters — men and birds — occupy the place of honor. There is no question that Raphael made the drawing "wrong" so that the final tapestry should be "right." He drew a left-handed Christ occupying the left extremity of the cartoon because he wanted the reversal, the final appearance, to be "right." One thing is sure: Raphael certainly did not intend to present Christ left-handed and, especially, giving his blessing with his left hand.

Another section of the tapestry (Fig. 121) depicts St. Paul preaching in Athens. We note that the Apostle occupies the space near the right border of the piece and that a statue of Mars, further left, holds a spear in his right hand and a shield in the left. A photograph of the cartoon (Fig. 122) shows these details in reverse. The apostle occupies the left side of the piece while Mars holds the spear in his left hand, the shield in the right. All this must be intentional. Raphael obviously knew what he was doing. Once more he made his drawing (cartoon) "wrong" so that the final artwork would be "right."

There are altogether seven of the original ten cartoons preserved. In all of them there are some elements which testify that Raphael was aware of the fact that the final version, the tapestry-version, would be a mirror-image of his drawing. (Unfortunately, I keep saying "mirror" although it has nothing to do with a mirror.) He made sure that this image (left and right "transposed" by the technicalities of tapestry weaving) would be the "correct" version — the version to be presented to the public.

I shall not analyze the rest of the tapestry panels and their respective cartoons. If you study the cartoons further (which is preferable) you can without guidance easily locate the left-handed details. For example, you will find that in the cartoon to the tapestry "The Calling of Peter" Christ is seen standing on the left side and handing the keys to Peter with his left hand. There is one tapestry section that is of some interest to the ophthalmologist, the one called "The Blinding of Elymas." The story, as told in the "Acts of the Apostles," deals with a "false prophet" (the name Elymas actually means "sorcerer" or "magician") who tries to prevent the conversion of a high Roman official by the Apostle Saul, the future Paul. As Wölfflin describes it, "Elymas has pressed forward toward the center… when the darkness fell upon him and he recoils, throwing out both hands and twisting his head upwards, the unsurpassed image of blindness." According to newer, more accurate translations (for example, *The New American Bible*) the blindness was temporary and was caused by the "stare" of Paul's eyes. (So it most likely was a case of hysterical blindness.) In the cartoon by Raphael's hand the blind man moves from right to left. Obvious association leads here again to Rembrandt and the story of Tobit, the blind man. In the Phaidon edition of *Rembrandt's Etchings* (to which I refer repeatedly) there are two related examples catalogued — both of them ultimately derived from the "Elymas" archetype. One of them (see Fig. 137) shows in this Rembrandt "version" the blind man running in the "wrong" direction, toward the left, toward a wall. But with etchings we are used to reversed directions. Etchings are "prints" and the artist might not find it necessary to take this into account during the preparation of the plate. This is certainly not the case with the Vatican tapestries.

No doubt Raphael was fully aware of the fact of direction in pictorial representations and of the preferable direction of action, and he wanted his spectators see his work "right." His well known "Madonna" paintings are examples of the planned symmetry in his compositions. A more-or-less isosceles triangle is the basic structure behind them with the Madonna occupying the apex of the triangle. The "Madonna with the Fish" (Fig. 123, in the Prado) is a fine example. On the left we see young Tobias with his miracle-fish and the angel Raphael. (Note the name Raphael. It in a way identifies the painter and the angel.) The right side of the composition is occupied by a picture of Mark the Evangelist and his symbol, the lion. The Madonna occupies the peak of the triangle. (We note that the Child is on the Evangelist's side.)

The "classic" example is, of course, the "Sistine Madonna," the paradigm of Raphaelic triangular, symmetrical composition (Fig. 124a), the Madonna with Child naturally occupying the apex of the triangle. The two sides of the triangle slope toward a male and a female figure, respectively. Is it truly just all symmetry with no element of action or movement?

We have to learn to see with Wölfflin's discriminating eye to realize that direction, specifically the direction left-to-right, is built into even this type of composition. Our gaze starts its move at left bottom — according to Weinstein* the most preferred starting point (The tiara here tells us, incidentally, that the figure we are going to look at is a pope.) His gaze, reinforced by our gaze, is carried upwards and toward the right to reach the Child and the Madonna's head at the apex of the triangle. (Note that in this case the Child is on the Pope's side of the picture-space and that in the previous example he was on the Evangelist's side — thus in both cases on the male side. I don't know if there is any symbolic significance to these details.) From here on his gaze sinks toward the lower right, toward the female figure whose downward gaze once more reinforces our gaze.

Incidentally, in my lectures I used to show this painting together with Mantegna's "Adoration of the Shepherds." (I liked to show the "Sistine Madonna" because "she" is so well known.) I used to show one slide in the "correct" projection (see Fig. 124a) and another one "left-and-right transposed" (Fig. 124b) and I had the audience guess which they thought was the "right" one. In the correct version our gaze hits the male character first. He knows already where and for whom to look. His boldly fore-shortened right arm and hand (truly a bravura-achievement!) invite the Madonna to look at us from her exalted position. She looks at us, the spectators, the unseen multitude of believers; she looks at the world. In the transposed version the female character is the one first seen. She occupies the left side of the picture. She looks downward, oblivious of or not even knowing about the central figures. The male character is in this case

*Weinstein, P. "Vision and the Art of Painting". Journal of Ophthalmology (Hungarian), 1958, p. 203.

located in the right half of the picture-space. He looks upward, his gaze collides with the spectator's gaze which by that time is already on its downward course. He looks supplicant. Only belatedly will the tiara tell us who the male figure is.*

It is an amazing picture this "Sistine Madonna." Too bad "she" is so overexposed. I could not help knowing her even in a small town in pre-World War I rural Hungary. All kinds of devotional objects and cheap reproductions of religious art were all I could see in the show window of the "Catholic Bookshop." The "Sistine Madonna" and Dürer's "Praying Hands" were among them. Years later "she" was one of the great objects of art I first saw "in the flesh." It was in 1921 or 1922. The occasion was my first foray into a dreamland — Weimar, Germany. Strangely "she" did not impress me at that time; the Giorgione "Venus" in the same room, on the opposite wall, extinguished her. By the way, this amazing picture also has some surrealistic elements — details that cannot possibly exist in the same space at the same time for either optical or contextual reasons.

Let me return to the tapestry section, "The Miracle of the Fish," (see Fig. 119) and look at it through Wölfflin's eyes. It is one of his well chosen examples to demonstrate the simultaneous (and harmonious) presence of both classic repose and emotion-motivated action in the same pictured event. We are presented with a Raphaelic triangle. However, in this particular case it is a figure of secondary importance that occupies the apex of the triangle. At the lower end points of the triangular substructure we see figures of vastly differing significance — an unimportant subject, the oarsman of one of the fishing boats, on the left end (the "gaze-starting" end) of the picture, and the most important subject, Christ, at the right end (the "gaze-finishing" end). The two persons do not seem to be related by any action. They exist simultaneously in the picture's *zero* time. With all this seeming stability in space and time the picture is anything but symmetrical or motionless in its spiritual content. The conspicuous character occupying the apex of the triangle is turned toward the right; all of his emotion-filled gestures point toward the right. All the action, all the drama occurs between the triangle's two ends. And it is not a frozen moment of the action that the artist depicts. Those two acting characters of the drama — Simon, the future Peter, and Andrew, his brother — are "stupefied" by their recognition of the divine presence. They must have both risen to their feet to approach this presence and to throw themselves at his feet. Simon is already kneeling (coming to rest) while Andrew is still on his feet, moving vehemently. He too will be soon falling upon his knees. The fact that the action component runs in a definite direction makes it possible to bring different times (Simon's just-past and Andrew's still-future actions) within the simultaneity of the design.

*I used the trick of right-left reversal once already and also in connection with a well-known lady's portrait. However, there I referred only to the change of the appearance of the eyes (see Fig. 42).

Fig. 126

Fig. 125

Fig. 127

Fig. 128

Musicians

After this rather heavy dose of "classic" art and art appreciation in the grand Wölfflin style, let us turn toward a simpler, nonetheless related instance — to some fine paintings by an American artist, William Mount, active around the middle of the last century. Besides being an excellent painter and draftsman, Mount was an accomplished musician. He liked musicians as subjects. In one of these paintings (Fig. 125) the violinist is shown fingering with the left hand and holding the bow with the right in the usual manner. In an exhibition in the Whitney Museum some years ago I came across the painting shown in Figure 126. Here the bow is held by the left hand and the fingering is done by the right. This strange painting evoked my curiosity and I did a little reading on the subject. I learned that the artist kept an excellent filing system: every item of his artistic output was named and catalogued. This particular painting is named "Right and Left." It was commissioned by the Paris firm, Goupil, who planned to publish colored prints based on this painting. Obviously Mount was faced with the same problem as Bruegel and many others before him. He painted a portrait of a left-handed musician knowing that in the process of reproduction it would turn out to be just "right."

By the way, bowing the violin with the left hand is an almost unheard of occurrence. In the hundreds of concerts I have attended in more than 50 years, I have only seen one left-handed violinist. I personally interviewed him,* and he told me that he suffered an injury to the left hand as a child and was forced to finger with the right hand. I am sure that there are many left-handers among the hundreds of violinists, violists and cellists I saw playing. How they handle their instruments is, I am sure, mainly a product of rigorous training. The guitar is a more popular, more leisurely instrument, and I met lately several youngsters who strum their instrument with the left hand. (They turn the instrument 180 degrees and rearrange the strings.)

There are two fine portraits of guitar players in the Metropolitan Museum of Art. One of the players, "Mezzetin" by Antoine Watteau (Fig. 127), holds his instrument in the usual way. In the portrait of the guitarist by Manet (Fig. 128) we have an example of a person handling his instrument with his left hand.

*The case is reported in some detail in my book *On Writing, Reading and Dyslexia* (1973).

Fig. 129

Fig. 130

Fig. 131

Brushstrokes

Once more let us turn our attention to the subject of left-handedness and art. Leonardo da Vinci comes immediately to mind. Everyone familiar with the process of drawing will easily recognize that Leonardo's drawings were mostly (maybe exclusively) done with the left hand. All one has to do is to look at the direction of the shading lines which in Leonardo's drawings run from upper left to lower right. A famous example is the haunting, mysterious face of a beautiful woman (Fig. 129) as only he could draw them. That the direction given the shading lines is not just happenstance is best attested by Figures 130 and 131. The subject is horses. One horse is turning right, the other left. Irrespective of the direction in which the horses are moving the shading lines still run in the direction of upper left to lower right.

This type of line is not, or only rarely, discernible in paintings. The artists of the Renaissance did not like their brushstrokes to show. In fact this was sometimes very much frowned upon. There are some oils by Cézanne in which the direction of the individual brushstrokes is conspicuous. Today we have the feeling that this adds to rather than detracts from the force of these pictures. (And then just think of those brushstrokes of van Gogh!) In some watercolors by Cézanne we can see the direction gravity pulls the still-wet pigment suspension. It is a marvel! You feel that "you are there" and "you can see" how the artist is working. (It is one of the greatest experiences an art-lover can have.) Chardin's self-portraits (see Figs. 21 and 22) were done in pastels, a medium clearly revealing the right-handed character of his strokes. Still it is mostly in drawings with a pencil that shading lines best give away which hand was used.

The next example (Fig. 132), a drawing by Raphael, tells us that the artist was right-handed. His shading lines run from upper right to lower left. The same holds true for Rembrandt (Fig. 133) who also was right-handed.

At first sight there is something puzzling about our next examples (Figs. 134 and 135), both by Rembrandt. It appears that the shading lines run from upper left to lower right. Why?

I think nobody has ever suggested that Rembrandt was left-handed or even ambidextrous; he certainly was not. He was right-handed and he drew his shading lines habitually from right to left. The answer to our question is that these pictures are etchings, not drawings. They are (as I rather sloppily but habitually refer to them) "mirror"-images of drawings. The direction of the shading lines is one of the criteria by which to decide whether an artist is right-handed or left-handed. But we have to make sure at first that they are drawings — not etchings, engravings, lithographs or any other kind of print from some interim surface (for instance, a copper-plate) upon which the artist originally drew an "image."

If what we plan to obtain is an etching we need first to have a drawing — a drawing on a copper-plate, but still a drawing. If the artist is a right-hander, then the shading lines applied to the plate will continue to be running from upper right to lower left. Nothing has changed so far. The process of printing from the plate will "transpose" the plate's right and left. The plate has to be "turned around" to face the paper. It has to be turned around in the third dimension and not "rotated" in a two-dimensional plane. Thus, in an etching-portrait (be it the image of the artist or of someone else) the shading lines will generally appear "left-handed." Moreover, one can expect that a right-handed artist works usually under light coming from his left. (We can bet on this in Rembrandt's case.) Consequently, in etchings it will be the side of the face that is nearer the left edge of the paper that will appear to be in the shadow. *As if* (I repeat: *as if*) the source of illumination had been on the right.

It will certainly not be difficult to find pertinent examples in Rembrandt's *oeuvre*, whether they be etching-portraits of people or of himself. The etching just considered (see Fig. 134) is an example. To summarize (and all this holds true only for the right-handed artist): "left-handed" shading lines, apparent illumination coming from the right (either or both) are characteristics of etchings (or any print). Or to put it differently: in an etching-portrait (any portrait-"print," be it a self-portrait or the portrait of someone else), the side of the head that is nearer the right border of the paper usually appears to be better illuminated. (Looking at examples among the illustrations in any art book there can be no doubt that this is the case.) For painted portraits (including drawings) the opposite holds: it is the side of the head nearer the left border of the picture-space that is in the light, be it a self-portrait or the portrait of someone else.

There is something peculiar about self-portrait etchings. And it bears repetition: a self-portrait drawing or painting is a transferred image of the mirror-image of the artist's own features. If the drawing is made on a copper-plate, then the printing will trans*pose* this trans*ferred* image. The image of the right half-face of the artist which *on the plate* is nearer the right edge of this plate, will now have its imprint nearer the left margin of the printed paper. Looking at his own etching-self-portrait the artist will note something strange. He will see his own face in a way he has never seen before (in a drawn or painted self-portrait). ("Never" meaning only before photography was invented.) A self-portrait etching might actually strike the artist as being strange, false, schizophrenic, alienated — the way we see ourselves in a double-mirror although we appear to ourselves the way we must appear to all people except ourselves.

That most famous of Rembrandt's self-portrait etchings (Fig. 136a). makes us happy because we see the Master drawing with a right-looking right hand. It might have made the artist happy because he too saw himself portrayed a right-hander while it also permitted him to draw his face on the plate exactly the way he saw himself (hands included) in the mirror. But, as his face revealed, he was not very happy. This, however, is another story and one that deserves a chapter for itself.

Fig. 134

Fig. 135

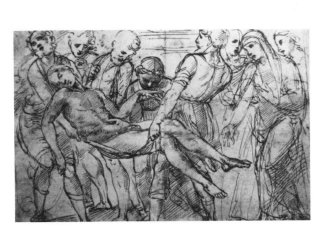

Fig. 132

Fig. 133

Fig. 136a

5 AN OPHTHALMOLOGIST LOOKS AT A "REMBRANDT" BY REMBRANDT. ALSO SOME FURTHER NOTES ON ETCHINGS

Anybody who knows anything about Rembrandt, the painter, seems to know about his "Laughing Self-Portrait" (see Fig. 76). Anybody who knows anything about Rembrandt's etchings seems to know about the one called "Rembrandt Drawing at a Window" (see Fig. 136a). These two works of art must be somehow unique. One should, of course, always be suspicious when one learns about "generally accepted" values. But in these cases even those knowledgeable seem to agree. As I have already mentioned, the "Laughing" painting is the only self-portrait I have remembered ever since I read about it and saw a reproduction of it in Emile Verhaeren's "Rembrandt." It was the first book I read while still in my teens about the Master. I must have been impressed by Verhaeren's commentary on it. Then here we have Gasser, the venerable editor of the volume *Self-Portraits*. He had some seventy of Rembrandt's painted self-portraits to choose from and he chose the "Laughing" one. So there must be something unique about that picture and, as we shall find out, in some ways it really is. For sure, this was the one where he did not follow his own rather strict routine. But is that all? Could it be all?

And what about the etching? I have the great new Phaidon edition of *Rembrandt's Etchings* in front of me — two volumes, the complete work, more than three hundred items. Among them are some thirty self-portraits. In this vast *opus* the learned editor, Ludwig Muntz, chose as the particular item to be the frontispiece to his first volume, the 1648 etching: "Rembrandt Drawing at a Window."

One of the memorable exhibitions of Rembrandt's etchings (and for me one of the most memorable art-events of a lifetime) was the 1969 exhibition called "Rembrandt: Experimental Etcher," in the Morgan Library in New York. (It was also shown at the Boston Museum of Fine Arts.) As the frontispiece to its well-documented catalogue, the editor also chose the same etching; a State I print, I might add, as seen in Figure 136a. The cover of the paperback edition (one of my prized possessions) carries a "pop-art" version, a four-times-eight repetition of the same etching. (The learned eye will, of course, notice that each row is a different "State" of it.) So there must be something unique to this etching. (I have to apologize here for the association, but this book cover reminds me of that ill-famed portrait by Andy Warhol of Marilyn Monroe — now in New York's Whitney Museum. It is amazing how flexible our taste is and how, after a while, we accept certain aberrations as not entirely without merit.)

Rembrandt is a peculiar kind of sphinx — he seldom speaks but he always tells. And it seldom is plain straight talk. No Sherlock Holmes can solve a crime if its perpetrator does not "tell," does not (inadvertently in most cases) leave some telling clue behind. As we have discovered in the case of that "Laughing" portrait, there is a piece of cloth left shining in the picture's darkness. He tells us by this clue that the light in that instance came from the artist's right. Why? He must have had a reason. We shall never know.

And now here we have this other enigma, the etching of all etchings — "Rembrandt Drawing at a Window." What is its secret? What makes it so unique? Did the Master leave any "clues" (planted or inadvertent) behind?

But first let me say that even with the impressive looking number (I give their number as 30) of etchings, they occupy a minor place in Rembrandt's "autobiography without words." Most of the self-portrait etchings are small, inconsequential bits of paper. Some of them are rather ugly looking, with that queer darkness covering up half the face. (I mean, of course, the half nearer to the *left* border of the paper.) This clue (remember, they are etchings) implicitly tells us that the source of light was, as usual for him, on the artist's left. What purpose these bits of paper served is not clear. Maybe the artist wanted to try out some new needle, some different acid or whatnot. Maybe he wanted to do a quick sketch on the plate and, obviously, his own person was the nearest available "model." There are not more than half-a-dozen self-portrait etchings that would merit any attention. I should not tarry with them too long. I chose Figures 134 and 135 as my first examples for the good reason that they represent the "left-handed" shading lines quite well. However, this should not bother us any longer. Shading lines of etchings look "left-handed" and by now we understand why.

One happy and uncomplicated etched self-portrait is known as "Rembrandt With Raised Saber," dated 1634. The half of the face nearer the left border of the paper is in the shade, as expected in an etching. A saber, like a pipe or cigarette, can be held in either hand. The whole picture could not be nicer. Two other self-portrait etchings are, clearly, studies; they are mirror-images of each other, prompted by Rembrandt's coming across Raphael's portrait of Castiglione (see Fig. 31). I guess the Master wanted to find out how one arm and hand or the other is going to look when shown resting on a balustrade. Still, in a minority of cases it is the half of the face nearer to the paper's left border which is better illuminated. The artist might have done some experimenting with illumination or possibly tried to draw a picture somewhere outside the studio where the light happened to come from his right side. But there is another even more important detail that must have caught the Master's attention. *The hand in the "Window" etching that looks like a right hand (anybody else's right hand) is actually the image of the artist's right hand — his drawing hand.* For an artist with a life-long obsession about left-handedness, this must have been a more than just pleasant discovery.

So here we are with that etching self-portrait "Rembrandt Drawing at a Window" (see Fig. 136a). It is, no question, different from almost all other self-portrait etchings. Let us see the illumination. The side of the face nearer to the left edge of the paper is the side that is in the light and this is even emphasized. The source of the light is a big, conspicuous window which occupies considerable picture-space on the extreme left. There is no other example among the Master's etching-portraits in which a window or any other source of light would have been even indicated. This self-portrait with the window is certainly unique. Should it be this fact, a mere technicality, that makes this etching so great? *The* paradigm? *The* etching to be chosen from all etchings? I don't know. Our real question is how did the artist do it? How did he manage to arrive at an etching self-portrait in which the half face nearer to the left border of the paper is illuminated — seemingly against all the rules of "optics" — and in which the hands do not look like mirror-images? Did the Master, by any chance, simply cheat? (He did that sometimes with painted self-portraits.) Did he, like some crafty culprit, perchance plant the window as a false clue in the wrong place? No. He did neither.

"Elementary, Doctor Watson!" I exclaimed one evening, emulating Sherlock Holmes, when I suddenly recognized the window as the telling clue and then saw the pieces of the puzzle fall into their proper place. "Elementary!" First, Rembrandt would never draw a picture of his "self" without using a mirror and, second, the picture in question is an etching, so right and left were reversed *after* (let me repeat: *after*) he finished drawing on the plate. "Elementary." A window near the left border of an etching indicates that this source of light actually was on the artist's right side, while he worked on the plate. Once this is taken to be true, the rest follows logically; the source of light on his right illuminated the right half of the artist's face, the side which *in the mirror* appeared to him to be nearer to the right edge of the mirror. He copied this on the plate. Hence, in the print-version the illuminated half of the face is nearer to the left border of the paper. Also the window is even farther to the left. No mystery, no cheating. No psycho-history or only that type of psycho-history which assumes that the Master was seeing and thinking while working. He was possibly even pleased when he noticed his drawing hand *within the etching's picture-space* and not looking like a left hand any longer. But somehow he was still unhappy, I guess, since he did not cherish the idea of illumination coming from the right side while the right hand works. And it seems that he was timid rather than boastful with those hands. In the first version (State I) (see Fig. 136a) he drew a bare outline of hands, filling in, filling in slowly, as things went along into later states.

Figure 136b represents State II of the "Window" etching. Comparison with State I reveals some additions, among them a signature and some shading lines ("left-handed," as expected) around the signature and in the upper left corner of the windowsill. The artist also did some finishing (in State I) of the barely sketched hands. In the last known state (State V) (Fig. 136c) we find something unexpected: the artist placed a rather undistinguished landscape into the much too empty window space, something which I doubt he had really seen while working on the earliest state of the plate. Rembrandt did such beautifully rich landscape etchings when he had a "model" from which to work. (I mean, of course, when he drew a landscape "from nature.") And he was very poor at cheating. He also kept on fiddling with the distribution of light over the face. (Even the expert commentators are vague about the purpose or the effect of these changes.) He obviously was not quite as happy as we could have expected him to be. There must have been something eerie in the picture which, I guess, he could not rationalize. There must have been something strange in that picture of "self" that looked at Rembrandt from the paper's plane. "He" was kind of strange, though he was "Rembrandt" at the same time. "He" (I mean the "Rembrandt" of the etching) looks uneasy, uncomfortable, constrained to me, a spectator of today, as I imagine "he" must have looked at him (I mean Rembrandt) and as "he" keeps on looking at us through all these centuries, in that mysterious give-and-take of this fascinating piece of work. It is a creation, I keep telling myself, of the artist's hand but still it is strange. A portrait of "self"? Yes. A "mirror"-image? No, not quite. Not any more. And it must have been the "strange one" (I mean "the man in the picture") who kept on looking at Rembrandt (I mean the artist) as soon as the first state of the etching came off his press. It was that "strange one" who made him (the artist) make alterations from state to state, especially in the distribution of light over the face, confusing alterations, the purpose of which we can hardly grasp.

Rembrandt certainly knew his own mirror-image. He must have known it. He transferred it on canvas or paper so many times. Always (certainly almost always) he had the light come from the left. This time for some reason the light must have come from Rembrandt's right and illuminated the right half of his face. But then our great Master (the

Experimental Etcher) also decided for the copper-plate, for a print. And that is when he must have found out that there was a difference. That "strange one," who was his (Rembrandt's) creature, was a "Rembrandt," but not the mirror-image which a self-portrait is by definition supposed to be. Rembrandt *did* transfer his mirror-image but he transferred it onto a copper-plate. He did it just the way he had done it in his drawing- and painting-portraits for years and years. But now this was an etching-image, an etching self-portrait. And that, as it turns out, is not quite the same. In the preparation of an etching one more procedure is added and seemingly Rembrandt never realized, never rationalized, that this procedure produces a picture that *derives* from a mirror-image, his (the artist's) mirror-image, but in the strictest terms of logical geometry is *not* a mirror-image anymore. They are *incongruent*.

I guess Rembrandt never read a textbook on optics and he could not have known about topology. I don't know how much he knew about Dürer. But he must have known from his own experimenting that when he looked at himself (more precisely at the image of himself) *in* a mirror and then lifted his "felt" right hand* then the hand which he saw in the mirror lifting itself was the one nearer to the right border of the mirror. And when he blinked with his "felt" left eye (or closed this left eye) then it was the eye in the mirror nearer the left border of the mirror that blinked. The mirror-image was a quasi-part of his being and inseparable from it. The transfer of the mirror-image on any kind of picture-surface (plate included) never raised any problems in topology, since mirror-image and transferred image were congruous arrangements. But that added procedure, the printing, disrupted this intimate bond. When the Master looked at the finished product, the "etching self-portrait," he must have immediately realized that what he was looking at was, in some manner, incongruous with those self-images he was so familiar with. In what manner? I guess he did not, at least at the beginning, know how and why

Fig. 136b

Fig. 136c

*I realize the anachronism. The concept of a body-image or of sensory-motor spatial localization did not yet exist at Rembrandt's time.

"it" looked like "him." "It" carried his features. "It" was dressed as he was. But at the same time "it" also looked like the picture of any other person.

So there was more to it than just the unusual direction of illumination that made the "Window" etching strange, alien, and alienated. Even if the light had come from the "right" direction, i.e., from the "correct" or left direction, the "self" in the self-portrait etching would have still remained alien to him. And even that was not all. While painted self-portraits like painted portraits were familiar to him, he was (he must have been) as confused as the rest of us by an etched self-portrait — being that it is the image of the image of an image which, if we think of it, produces the final image on our retina. Even identifying those hands (those blessed hands that finally looked "right") is not easy. It still requires some added thinking. So let's see: the hand-image I see nearer the left border of the etching is the transposed "image" of a hand that, by the artist's tools, was etched upon (or engraved into) the surface of a plate (the difference is purely technical) nearer to the right border of this plate. In its turn, this plate-image of a hand is the transferred congruous image of a mirror-image, specifically of the mirror-image of the artist's own right hand. No wonder it is confusing. But this is still not all. Far from it. If I myself, Ego (let's call it [E]), face anybody else except myself (let's call it [non-E]) then it is anybody else's left hand that is opposite my right hand. This is the way the world is organized. But he has to face me for this. Think of Velázquez's "Breda" (see Fig. 100a): the Dutchman and the Spaniard meet face to face. The right hand (with keys) of the former is opposite the left hand (with Marshal's staff) of the latter. No glass-plate, no wall between them. This is the way our world is organized. There is but one exception and that is everybody's own mirror-image facing him in its (or from its) mirrored space. This one exception causes even the experts to get confused about Dürer's left eye or Reynolds's left and right hand. This one exception is the mirror-image of one's self. This image we could mark [-E]. In the case of the "Window" etching, something unexpected seemed to Rembrandt to have happened. It was something technical, that etching business — it was thought of as a new way of being able to produce multiple images to satisfy a market. But suddenly it looked as if that impenetrable barrier, the looking glass, the zero-surface between [E]-space and [-E]-space would have been broken through by that mere "technicality." The etching was an image of self, produced by himself. Still, that mere technicality somehow made it all sort of indeterminate. An "incubus." We could not call what he saw [non-E]. It was an image of self and obviously a derivate of his own mirror-image. But the right arm and hand of this incubus now appeared to be opposite Rembrandt's own left hand. A surrealistic (forgive the anachronism) right hand of "Rembrandt" holding a pen to draw a picture of Rembrandt. Could "he" (the "stranger") stretch out his right hand to shake the right hand of his creator? No mirror, no impenetrable barrier between self and self's image. This must have been disturbing to realize. Almost frightening. It was not worth the confusion. No wonder this is the only example of a major, formal, self-portrait etching by Rembrandt. He lived some twenty years longer; he did some of his greatest painted self-

Fig. 137

portraits. He also kept on experimenting with etchings, but he never made another statement in the medium self-portrait print. On the other hand the technique made him free. Etchings became his tool for creating the grandest and as yet unsurpassed body of Dutch-Protestant religious art. But all this is not in the ophthalmologist's field any longer. It will be more useful to review, tabulate and clarify.

So, assuming that the light comes from the artist's left, this is the way it goes:

(1) In the painted portrait of any person, except one's self, the portrait-hand nearer the *left* border of the canvas is the image of that person's *right* hand. (The half of the face nearer the left border of the canvas is illuminated.)

(2) In a painted self-portrait, the portrait hand nearer the *left* border of the canvas is the image of the artist's *left* hand. (The half of the face nearer the left border of the canvas is illuminated.)

(3) In a portrait etching of any person except one's self, the hand nearer the *left* border of the paper is the image of that person's *left* hand. (The half of the face nearer the left border of the paper is in the shade.)

(4) In a self-portrait etching the hand nearer the left border of the paper is the image of the artist's *right* hand. (The half of the face nearer the left border of the paper is in the shade.)

(5) Finally, self-portrait paintings and self-portrait etchings are incongruous. No manipulation will make them cover each other.

The second point of my tabulation shows the most intimate relations between the painter and the painting, the drawer and the drawing. This is seen in Dürer's drawings; in that important moment in the history of self-portraiture when young Dürer, looking into a mirror, lifted his *right* hand (why on earth did he not retain that pen!) and saw a strange and incongruous hand moving in the *right* half of the mirror-space. He discovered the "mirror-image" and succeeded in quasi-nailing a copy of it, the mirror-image of his right hand to the *right* half of his sketching paper.

With the introduction of the printing process into the making of self-portraits, all this intimate, half-conscious, almost organic relationship was broken. Yes, etchings, or prints present some problems. They have to be expected. A "print," whatever the technique of its production, is one step (one fateful step) removed from what the artist actually saw and drew. (Should I say from "reality"?) It is some kind of a temporary interim surface (like a copper-plate) that carries the actual physical tracings of the artist's hand.

And here we might for a moment return to the problem of direction in depicted scenarios. We can assume that print-making has not greatly changed an artist's habits or working conditions. He is still right-handed and the light usually comes from his left side. The fact remains that having turned to printing, he cannot present his story by direct and straight drawing (or painting) any longer. He must do it *via* an intermediary (e.g., *via* etching a copper-plate). So although he drew his story in the left-to-right direction, the story in the finished "print" version will run the

Fig. 138a

Fig. 138b

opposite way. Bruegel or Mount who worked for the engraver or Raphael who worked for the tapestry weaver took this fact into account. But Rembrandt, it seemed, was not too interested. He was certainly fussy about the direction of the light under which he worked. But about the direction of the story in the presented version he was not at all dogmatic. A good example is our familiar Figure 137, one of the etchings dealing with the subject of the blind Tobit. He looks like he is running against a wall on the left. (He turned over his wife's spinning wheel in his rush.) His cane is in his left hand. The light appears to be coming from the right. Left and right have obviously been transposed by the printing process. This is responsible for those dark areas over the half-face nearer to the left border of the paper. (Needless to say that while the artist worked the light came from the left.)

A few words finally on the problem of "states" of etchings. That blind Tobit etching (see Fig. 137) exists essentially in only one state. It is a gem, a little masterpiece as it is. Nothing needs to be added. The room, the *ambiance*, are all given in clear Albertian perspective. Look at the door frame, the door-head, the threshold. Try and draw lines across. You might not believe it but you will find a rather accurately placed vanishing point. The movement is brisk, the action directed. Yes, toward the left. But that did not seemingly bother Rembrandt.

In general, early states of etchings tell us more about things the artist actually saw: mostly people (models), the ambiance. Later states concentrate on messages rather than information. This simple relationship usually holds for Rembrandt's more ambitious etchings, especially the great religious plates. An etching of State I might tell us what the artist actually saw: a model, a room, some realistic details. Then the artistic purpose overtakes. Some plates were "overworked" many times so that much of the original imprint has actually vanished. Plates from which later states were printed don't necessarily show what the artist originally saw even if they (the plates) are still in readable condition. Very few of the important plates are preserved in such an early state as our blind Tobit. The deeper the Master's spiritual commitment was, the more thorough are the changes. But this, I am afraid, is not ophthalmology any longer. So let me finish by presenting two states of one of the greatest Rembrandt etchings: "The Entombment" (Fig. 138a) is State I. Figure 138b is State IX. Not much of the "right-handed" shading of State I has remained. The perspective background has practically disappeared. The Man in the coffin is "The Light" (*his* words) and all around is darkness.

6 EL GRECO

El Greco (Domenikos Theotokopoulos) belongs among those artists whose name is known even to people who otherwise know little about art. Many of the ophthalmologists to whom I have lectured about visual physiology are in this group. (Fewer lately, however, than 25 years ago. Things in America have changed for the better and art appreciation is certainly one of them.) At least they have heard about El Greco's alleged astigmatism, about the distortions in El Greco's pictures, especially the elongations of the human figure, which, supposedly were caused by astigmatism. Thus, after I had become known (or notorious) as one who likes to use art slides to explain some point in visual physiology, I almost anticipated such questions as: "Do you think El Greco had astigmatism?" Or simply: "Are you going to talk about El Greco?" I usually tried to get away from the subject and assured my listeners that that ghost had already successfully been laid to rest and that, as the best authorities now seem to agree, there is no way to prove from El Greco's *oeuvre* that he had astigmatism. Moreover, I added, these authorities more or less also agree that it is almost impossible to tell from any drawn or painted design whether its designer had or did not have astigmatism or any other optical distortion of the shape (note the word "shape") of his "ocular" image. According to one quite frequently invoked and seemingly most logical argument, a person who on account of, say, astigmatism sees a "real" circle as a vertically elongated ellipse will have to draw (to us, normals) a normal-looking circle in order to see it elongated, i.e., the way he is used to seeing what we call "circles." In a sentence: while copying a circle a draftsman will draw a circle in the shape of the image of that circle in his eye. Yet, this is not quite true. Sometimes a timid voice in me asks: are there different degrees of truth? But then I quickly stop questioning. There would be little purpose in my giving here any history of the sometimes heated but mostly interesting controversy. What I used to do in later years was to quote Trevor-Roper's exposition on the subject. It was both for me and for the usual audience of future eye specialists, the easiest obtainable and the easiest understood formulation of "the great argument, the argument against." The quotation is as follows:

. . . the artist paints what he sees and the subject will correspond to the rendering, however much they are both altered by a misshapen eye into a distorted percept within the artist's brain. In other words, if he sees a flattened or elongated world, the likeness of it that he puts onto the canvas, in order to appear equally flattened or elongated to him, will in fact be depicted with its proper dimensions.

My distinguished colleague also clearly points out some of the limitations of this statement which he calls:

. . . essentially but not entirely true; an astigmatic does sometimes, to some extent, distort along the line of his astigmatism . . . .

I think only someone with Trevor-Roper's background, an ophthalmologist trained in the psycho-neurology of vision, could ever see the limitations. Indeed (as our author stresses) our assessment of the world is not only by "sight" but also by "feel." We orient ourselves both "haptically" ("by touch") and "kinetically" ("by potential for action") not merely by vision. And he also points out the possible difference between a person's copying (when he "makes a facsimile") and drawing (which he does "out of his head"). So, to repeat, that great argument so frequently invoked in discussions about El Greco is only "essentially but not entirely true."*

*The terms in quotation marks are borrowed from Trevor-Roper. To give him separate credit for each and every quote would be almost impossible.

What is Astigmatism?

Since some of my readers are non-ophthalmologists I should explain what the term "astigmatism" means. A light-collecting lens (a convex lens) collects a beam of the sun's parallel rays into a point, a fleck, a spot — *stigma*, in Greek. It will do this if it is "spherical," i.e., having the same curvature in any and all cross-sections. Such a lens could be called "stigmatic," but the term "spherical" tells more. A lens that will not collect a beam of light rays into a spot (specifically a lens that does not have equal curvatures in all cross-sections) is conveniently called "astigmatic" while the condition is called "astigmia" or "astigmatism." An astigmatic lens (or eye) cannot project sharp images of all details onto a screen (its retina). The retinal image in an astigmatic eye is mainly blurred. It is also out of shape in some specific manner. Some authorities prefer to use the term astigmatism only in reference to the eye. Spectacle lenses with unequal refraction power in different cross-sections are (not quite accurately) called "cylindrical."

But let us return to our paradigm circle. We can, I guess, all agree with Trevor-Roper that drawing a circle is a visually controlled activity — "essentially, but not entirely." There are also some musculo-sensory and some musculo-kinetic factors involved. And this will (as seen in the just given example) tend to add a vertical "feel" to the actually executed design.

So here we are. Here we have an argument — the great foolproof argument "against." In its light it looks just about impossible that some optical distortion (e.g., astigmatism) should manifest itself in an abnormal manual tracing — especially when "copying," i.e., "drawing a facsimile" from life. (And this argument should close all debate.) Still, we reserved for ourselves a kind of an escape clause — that "feel" of the hand. It is an escape clause with unpredictable consequences. Practically all of our non-visual space perception could be covered by it. And then there are some further questions. Let us once more consider when this particular type of astigmatism causes us to have vertically elongated retinal images.* Can we ever "see" a circle? Do we perchance choose a flattened ellipse for our "seen" circle? What happens when we rotate an ellipse? And what do we draw for a "circle" when we do not "copy" it but draw it "out of our heads"?

---

*However hard I try to be accurate I cannot avoid some inaccuracies. So I just want to mention that "ocular" and "retinal" are not really interchangeable, though I catch myself using the words in that manner. The usual astigmatism is a fault of the refracting system of the eye. It is "ocular," rather than "retinal."

We can also build a rather good case against any kind of astigmatism theory — at least as far as El Greco is concerned — from the evidence of El Greco's *oeuvre* itself. Both Goldscheider, the editor of the Phaidon *El Greco*, and Trevor-Roper point at one of El Greco's best known paintings, "The Burial of the Count Orgaz," in Toledo (Fig. 139). There is no detail (with one possible exception) in this complex and representative picture to which the label, astigmatic distortion, could be pinned. I might add here that a sizable number of his portraits (especially the commissioned portraits) are not distorted astigmatically. I have already mentioned several of them. But some repetition should not be resented.

One of my favorites among El Greco's portraits is "Portrait of a Painter," in Seville, Spain (Fig. 140). I have never seen it — not even a colored reproduction of it. However, the black and white reproduction tells us quite well how a painter with his tools of the trade will appear to us and to another painter. Note the fine, well-detailed right hand. It shows how a painter holds his brush just ready to paint. Once more I note how this hand represents a pendant to the mystery hand in Dürer's pen-and-ink self-portrait (see Fig. 54) — both present the palm-side of a right hand. The El Greco portrait tells us how *we* see a painter's hand when he is ready to paint. The Dürer drawing shows how *he* saw his right hand (ready to draw or paint, of course) in a mirror. And I note that the El Greco portrait also shows the natural position of an artist's left hand, his "palette" hand. And I cannot help thinking of the Reynolds self-portrait (see Fig. 89) which tells us how an artist sees his own palette-holding hand in the mirror. Suddenly, I note something else: the El Greco reproduction I have available is in black and white. All I see on the palette are four patches of (we must assume) different hues and one separate patch of white. I wish I knew what hues those four patches represent. It would give us some idea about pigments available at that time, and especially about the artist's views in reference to so-called "primary" colors and color mixing. (In the last century most artists counted three "primaries" — red, yellow and blue. The palette of this artist contains four patches. But one of them might be black.) This is a problem which I still hope to attack sometime.

There can be no question that this portrait was done "from life," in the Renaissance manner, following (of course, anticipating) the "Vermeer arrangement." The light is coming from the painter's (El Greco's) left. The model turns his head slightly toward his right (which leaves the left ear visible and still lets ample light fall on both halves of the model's face). This permits, at the same time, some delicate shading of the side opposite the source of light. The eyes are turned toward the model's left, fixating at the painter (El Greco). The eyes are delicately shaped, somewhat larger than normal (part of the enchantment of El Greco portraits) and their white is conspicuous on the side opposite the direction of gaze of both eyes.

El Greco spent some of his younger years in Italy; he learned some and did not forget all of it. He never forgot the "Vermeer arrangement." He was never very inventive in details. If you saw one or two of his (let me call them) commissioned portraits — especially of younger people — you would have seen them all. They are beautiful and also unmistakable. I imagine his customers were proud to own a portrait of themselves so unmistakably by him. A "sitter" wants his features to be recognizable. He wants his portrait to be "true to life." (But he wants only the beautiful half of the truth.) And he also wants there to be no question about the painter's identity. Thus, a fashionable portrait painter must be repetitious. Portraits by El Greco are a delight to look at. There is nothing in them that reminds us of astigmatism. Of course, there also are no reasons why the portraitist should have distorted anything (e.g., by elongation of details), or why he should have uglified a depicted person. He probably had all the reasons for the opposite.

Fig. 139

Fig. 140

Fig. 141

"The Burial of Count Orgaz"

Let me return to that famous painting "The Burial of Count Orgaz" (see Fig. 139) and to what it has to add to the astigmatism controversy.

There are two levels to the picture. In its smaller, lower half one can certainly see nothing distorted. (Was it perchance a commissioned painting?) It is all symmetry, sweet realism and no motion. (The corpse is in the middle and we cannot even anticipate whether it will be pulled right or left.) The dead Count, the long dead saints, the officiating priests, the elegant gentlemen forming the background (beautiful faces, beautiful hands), the pageboy in the foreground (a portrait of the artist's son) — all serene and (I cannot help repeating the words) all sweet, all beautiful. And then our gaze reaches the upper half of the canvas the subject of which is the spiritual self of the deceased man presenting itself to Christ and to St. Peter and the Virgin. Here we do encounter some (in fact only minor) exaggerations, mainly some elongations — as in the figures of Christ (at the very top of the painting) and of the Count's "soul." Could they be accounted for by astigmatism? They could not possibly — our experts tell us. If they were optical, physical, physiological, so the argument goes, they would have been seen in both levels of the painting. So those elongations must be planned, deliberate. Boldly generalizing from this example we will be tempted to say that this also might hold for wilder distortions in other paintings as well. Those distortions, too, might be planned and deliberate. Maybe all of them are just mannerisms, if the word is applicable to an artist of El Greco's rank. They are essentially baroque exaggerations of gestures: bodily movements to "express" moods (inwardly happenings) with added force. They were, we could say, "expressionistic" long before "expressionism" had been born. (And, in fact, it was to a great extent the flourishing German "expressionism" in art, and the adulation of German art historians that revived El Greco's work — for centuries, half-forgotten.)

The contrast between the lower and upper sections of "The Burial" is quite marked. Note the tranquility in the lower part and the lack of it in the upper. (The painting is not of the usual quadrangular shape. It ends in a semi-circle on the top. It has to fit into a niche. But this has nothing to do with astigmatism.) With all the unrest in the upper half of the canvas, the composition still reveals exact planning and discipline.

The "double-decker" arrangement (as I sometimes call it) of the picture was not anything new. We can find several examples of it in Wölfflin's book, and our artist could have easily seen one or more during his sojourn in Italy. The total effect of this particular painting still is serenity and harmony. It is of significance that the imaginary horizontal line that separates the two worlds does not slant in any direction as it should if some oblique astigmatic error were to play any role in the arrangement. El Greco, of course, could have used a rule or measuring tape to make the two end points of the horizontal dividing line as level as they really are. In fact that horizontal divider is not even imaginary. It is made up of a row of portrait heads, all of them of this world, all undistorted. (With excellent taste the artist added some undulation to this unique horizontal divider. But even this irregularity does not break the symmetry.)

We can also imagine a straight vertical line through the whole canvas, starting from the Christ figure at the top through the figure of St. Augustine (the one with the bishop's miter) and ending at the deceased Count's head at the vertical's lower end. (It is possible that the artist actually drew both the horizontal *and* the vertical dividing lines while the canvas still was naked. Maybe an X-ray picture would disclose it.) The vertical line would divide the painting into two practically symmetrical halves —each half quasi-built up of matching horizontal layers or tiers. In the tier nearest to the solitary figure we find the Virgin and St. Peter (with keys to let all those supplicants in). He and the Virgin are stationed on the left side and both are looking toward the right. The Count (his soul) and the multitude of supplicants behind him are stationed on the same level, on the right side. They all turn their faces toward the left. (I confess I don't understand all the details in the picture — for instance, all that commotion in the lower tiers of the upper half. I imagine I see a dove on the left and a whale on the right. They are most likely just clouds. I also imagine some miniature humans squirming. But again all this has nothing to do with astigmatism. And as far as planning and symmetry in the painting are concerned, I might add that even a memory of Raphael's "classic" triangular arrangement of the main characters is to be found at the top of the canvas: Christ, the solitary figure, is at the apex of the triangle, and the Virgin is below on the left. The "soul" of the Count (if that is what the naked kneeling figure symbolizes) occupies the triangle's lower right corner. This is the only "character" that is elongated out of proportion, elongated but not really distorted.

It should be of some interest that the Christ figure is actually smaller than the "soul." This is unusual. It was something "not done" in the Spain of the Grand Inquisitor. However, in this instance and due to the rounded top of the canvas the solitary figure at the upper end of the vertical divider is unique anyway. Our gaze has to be lifted to focus on it. The smallness just adds to the impression of farness. The figure is farther than even the heavenly part of the picture-space. He is beyond space.

By the way, Christ is the only figural mass that is self-luminant. ("I am the light of the world," he said.) Christ is also beyond the light that fills both spheres of the universe — the earthly and the heavenly. For the medieval "realist" Church they had equally "real" existences. (Did they still have it for a 17th century Spanish eye?) All other figures, including the Virgin, are illuminated by light coming from somewhere and falling somewhere. So faces, features, are painted in *chiaroscuro*. Even though he did not analyze it in a very scientific manner, El Greco knew how to use light, or illumination.

While such details (and comments thereon) are possibly still in the ophthalmologist's area of competence, I have gone far afield from the problem of El Greco's astigmatism to which "The Burial" painting adds little succor. The dead Count's soul in the heavenly half of the painting is elongated but not really distorted and certainly not as disjointed as are so many of the figures in those great religious panels on which rests (and I feel, justifiedly) El Greco's abiding fame. These distortions are the ones that actually spawned the idea of El Greco's astigmatism while there is no type of ocular astigmatism that could generate the kind of images we encounter in some of these pictures. Once more: I feel that these distortions are deliberate. They cover a well-planned outline (often symmetrical). Trevor-Roper tells us that X-ray studies of some El Greco paintings reveal a rigidly outlined structural design. The distortions were seemingly later added as El Greco kept on working on details.

Fig. 142

Fig. 143

More on El Greco

It was almost a shock to my audience when on one occasion and somewhat timidly (who am I to pass judgment on this great artist?) I ventured to say that El Greco was a poor draftsman and, also, a poor student of human anatomy and that at least some of his "distortions" could just as well be attributed to either or both of these factors. El Greco painted beautiful though somewhat flat, somewhat stylized, somewhat stereotyped and more than somewhat idealized portraits in which there is no trace of distortions — astigmatic or otherwise. I can add here that not much knowledge of anatomy is needed to paint a three-quarter length formal portrait — a head in a more or less standard position, over a standardized, white lace collar and some coverall black-on-black garment which must have been *de rigueur* for formal occasions among members of the establishment that El Greco came to Spain to serve. But then he also painted for them all those emotion-filled religious scenes. Here fantasy was expected to prevail over reality and expression over description. He used gestures to express emotions. He certainly did! But just as certainly he did not follow the precepts of greater men — Dürer and Leonardo — for whom study of the proportions of the human body and of its deeper structural anatomy was as much a "must" as the study of linear perspective. This Cretan painter, Theotokopoulos, laden with Byzantine tradition, learned a lot by exposure to the art of Italy while remaining a stranger to the land. He found a spiritual home in the still medieval Spain of St. Theresa and of Loyola where anatomy and perspective were not yet "musts" and possibly were even handicaps to both the portraying and the evoking of religious exultation. But that is not all. Some of it is just inept drawing; some of it straight and unforgivable ignorance of human anatomy, and beyond that an almost moral issue — a lack of humility.

I have already once used a paraphrased sentence on Moses from the Bible, applying it to Rembrandt. I want to do that now once more by saying that the man Rembrandt was the most humble one among men. Yes, it is humility that made Rembrandt the greatest among the great. He painted hundreds of portraits — men and women, rich and poor, mostly elderly. *Chiaroscuro* modelings of matured or decaying features. He never worked without a model. But there are no two faces in the universe that are identical. Hence the infinite, the inexhaustible variety of Rembrandt's portraits. Take Figure 141 — the golden glow of the short chain of pearls on the hat of a "Young Jew," now in Cleveland. What beauty. How simple. And how real. It is impossible to "invent" such a detail. El Greco would have never even noticed it. It just happened once. Rembrandt saw it, noted it and made the occasion timeless, deathless — hopefully for a thousand and more years.

As I have already mentioned in connection with his portrait paintings, El Greco was for quite some time exposed to Italian Renaissance art. He also acquired some knowledge of perspective at the same time. This is clearly seen in a few of his earlier, more realistic, less fantastic historical-religious paintings. Good examples are the two versions of "The Healing of the Man Born Blind" (Figs. 142 and 143). Both were done during his years in Italy. One is in Dresden and the other, in Parma. The background in both of them presents some buildings and colonnades "in perspective." In the Dresden version the display of the tiled floor and an extra step painted into the foreground add substantially to the three-dimensional impression. But he had to shift the Christ figure out of the center, to have sufficient room to show this "skill." We also see two good-sized sitting figures occupying (with some small allowance) the center of the canvas. They establish a mid-ground and add substantially to our feeling of depth in the picture. I have earlier in connection with Leonardo's "Annunciation" mentioned the illusion of several picture-layers, one behind the other — the illusion of stereoscopic depth in that painting. In the Dresden version of the El Greco painting we see a similar arrangement. The Christ group is lowest and nearest. (It also is the starter for our gaze.) The Pharisee "group" was shifted to the right and somewhat higher and thus appears farther. The two groups together establish a "foreground" and give the essential part of the story. The mid-ground figures are for the story irrelevant. But the establishment of mid-ground somewhat pushes the foreground figures even further forward. We see them (we feel we see them) almost in front of the picture-space. In the Parma version it is the Christ figure that occupies the geometric center of the picture. The two sitting characters lost their *raison d'être*: they are relegated into "insignificance." One has to look for them to find them. The Dresden version is the more painterly; the other version conforms better with tradition (or maybe some written or not-written rules of the "Holy Office"). The Son of God could not be in a sideshow.

As far as linear perspective is concerned, the two versions are similar. The action takes place in open air, way in front of the perspective display, which merely serves as an unessential (rather schematic) background decoration and takes no part in the happening.

There are several versions of "The Cleansing of the Temple" by El Greco in existence. They present much more complex perspective arrangements of floors, steps and especially columns, that include both background and foreground. In other words the action depicted now takes place *inside* the space displayed in perspective. The Minneapolis version (Fig. 144) was painted in Italy. So there is room in the painting for a couple of naked infants and a topless lady. In the versions done in Spain at least 20 years later (one in Cambridge, the other in the National Gallery, London), there is little change as far as perspective is concerned. Things have certainly not improved. But the formerly half-naked lady near the right border of the picture is now fully dressed (Fig. 145). And it is fortunate that the Christ figure seems to float rather than walk over the floor. He would otherwise stumble over some awkwardly placed furniture. It is just poor drawing, of course.

According to an old saying: when in Rome do as the Romans do. (And El Greco did, in fact, spend some of his Italian time in Rome.) He experimented with perspective for a while. But his heart was not in it. In his later work perspective as a space vehicle, as a framework for optical localization of details, is grossly disregarded.

And the astigmatism? All I can say is that in the paintings so far reviewed I have not found any sign indicating an optical error and no such distortions as could be attributed to astigmatism in El Greco's eye. To the El Greco paintings that are free of an "astigmatic error" we could add another group — the religious historical pictures of which I have just mentioned a few. So the thought shoots inescapably through my mind: *maybe that whole story about El Greco's astigmatism is just a legend.* Again and again we are reminded of those religious fantasy portraits and fantasy scenarios. Those saints, all those saints with all their elongations and disproportions! Those bodies ten times the length of the heads! Those disjointed, otherworldly gestures! Those asymmetric faces! Those dissociated, diverging, unfocused eyes! And those unwearable robes made of plaster-like fabrics with unbending folds! Yes, all those details are on the layman's mind whenever he speaks about distortions in El Greco's figures — believing as he does that some optical fault (we call it astigmatism) must have been causing them. The distortions are not astigmatism. They are distortions to which no optical explanation will fit. They are all mannerism. Yes, mannerism — but quite often of a deeply spiritual and always of a highly personal nature. And the strange ending of the story is that these great virtues are built upon inept draftsmanship and sometimes almost irritating ignorance of human anatomy. He certainly did not let his shortcomings grow into an inferiority complex. Our great El Greco, "The Greek," had both talent and a unique Levantine background. And there is no doubt that he did make the best of them.

Fig. 144

Fig. 145

7 STILL MORE ABOUT PAINTERS AND ASTIGMATISM. A SWEDISH OPTICIAN REKINDLES THE ISSUE.

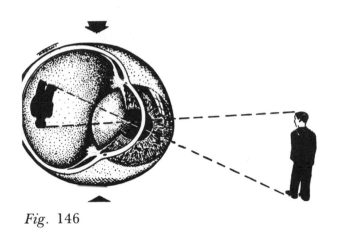

Fig. 146

Both parties to the El Greco dispute (believers and non-believers in the astigmatism theory) must have been impressed by a paper published in 1955 by O. Ahlström of Stockholm (an optician). The paper deals with the "eyesight" of six well-known Renaissance painters. As the author concluded from the analysis of certain aspects of their work, three of them — Leonardo, Raphael and Dürer — must have had "normal eyesight"; while the other three — Hans Holbein the younger, Lucas Cranach senior (or one of his associates, the "nude specialist"), and, finally, El Greco — must have had "ocular astigmatism."

As far as the "normals" are concerned (no criteria!) we shall agree without any further discussion. Raphael was the perfection which (to use the words of an old Hungarian adage) even our Creator can only on rare Fridays reach. And Leonardo? He was certainly "normal" as far as his eyes were concerned. From what we know of him, he had binocular single vision with stereopsis even though the technical terms for saying so were not yet developed. (He noted that with two eyes we can see "around" objects remarking, regretfully, that this is the kind of seeing the artist cannot duplicate on the picture surface.) And how about the "normalcy" of Dürer? There is certainly no sign in his *oeuvre* that could indicate his having had ocular astigmatism, although (as already mentioned earlier) he possibly had no binocular vision.

Of the three artists in whose paintings Ahlström discovered signs of "ocular astigmatism," I will, partly for the sake of brevity, neglect to discuss the Cranach case in any detail. I must confess that in spite of all the years spent in Germany — and all those German museums — I have never developed any personal feeling toward his work. (Then again, I have not really studied it.)

Obviously Ahlström had no clinical data from which to deduce that the three artists had astigmatism. His evidence is based on their works, on some distortions — mainly elongations — that he found to be characteristic of each artist's individual handling of his subject. The direction of these elongations was horizontal for Holbein, vertical for Cranach and slanting for El Greco.

Was it perchance unjustified to tell myself that El Greco's astigmatism could be just a legend? Surely Trevor-Roper did forewarn us and I repeat: "An astigmatic does sometimes, to some extent, distort along the line of his astigmatism." Maybe it is only sometimes, in some particular type of presentation, that astigmatism will show. Ahlström's examples are all portraits. Maybe a draftsman with an astigmatic eye does draw a circle when copying a circle. But maybe the visual acuity required for doing a portrait — details of the human face and details of the human figure — is of a higher order than "copying" a geometric figure.

Of Ahlström's trio, Holbein's case is the easiest to understand, and an illustration in Trevor-Roper's book (Fig. 146) explains (almost without words) how an artist's astigmatism could influence the shape of what his retina receives and what he then paints. This holds true especially for the human figure, for the human face, because of our fabulous ability to memorize, to recall and to differentiate human shapes. Obviously, the illustration is only diagrammatic. It abstracts one factor — call it the "shape-factor" — from the astigmatic disruption of the retinal image. As presented, it depicts the more commonly encountered type of ocular astigmatism (traditionally called astigmatism "with-the-rule") in which the refraction power of the eye is greater in a vertical meridian than in a horizontal — making the retinal image, e.g., of a human figure, somewhat "squat" (wider across), somewhat shorter vertically in proportion to its width.

The portrait of Henry VIII by Holbein is, according to Ahlström (Figs. 147a & b),* the typical example of a painting done by an artist afflicted (if that is the correct word) with that more common type of astigmatism. If the horizontal refracting meridian of the artist's eye has less power, then, as a consequence, the horizontal cross section of his retinal image is relatively wider. What the artist tells us in this portrait is what the refracting system of his eye told his retina: "The King in the picture is too broad for his height;" because of the retinal image produced by Holbein's astigmatic eye.

*This illustration from Ahlström's essay and Figures 150a & b and 152a & b are reproduced from Trevor-Roper's book. The left halves are photographs of the original artworks; the right halves were taken through an inverted special telescope: a concave and a convex cylindrical lens. This telescope shortened the Holbein painting in the horizontal and the El Greco portraits in an oblique meridian.

But is it really the artist's astigmatism that manifests itself in this particular painting? Maybe Holbein has as faithfully as possible under these unique and difficult circumstances simply registered one of his model's physical peculiarities. As Ahlström pertly noted: "One cannot help being impressed by the massive bulk of His Majesty."

In a recent book, *Tenements of Clay*, containing medical biographies of famous people (edited by the noted London ophthalmologist, Arnold Sorsby), we can read that Henry VIII was "enormously fat" in the last decade of his life (toward the end he had to be carried on a litter). Holbein's job as a court-painter was, no doubt, a difficult one: he must have tried to shape that "massive bulk" into an acceptable picture, "broad" but still "robust." What we know about the subject makes it (at least to a degree) justified that we question Ahlström's contention in this particular instance. However, there exist several other portraits by Holbein in which the "models" appear markedly (though not as extremely) broad-shouldered. Possibly there were two factors that mutually contributed to this: (a) an astigmatic shape-factor and (b) a misshapen "model," the King, who was "enormously fat." Holbein was a superb technician, an impeccable draftsman. So the abnormally wide, painted figure could in fact be what his retinal image actually told him.

I need not now describe in any detail the insipid nude by Cranach analyzed in Ahlström's paper. The astigmatism (if any) of this artist must have been, in all respects, the opposite of the one just discussed — a case of astigmatism "against-the-rule." The refracting power of the artist's eye must have been, in this case, less powerful in the vertical meridian making his nudes appear too slender. Trevor-Roper is unimpressed. Let me quote: "Cranach was one of the many artists whose vertical elongations were (wrongly) attributed to astigmatism." He is even more emphatic in his note on a lovely Modigliani nude. He tells us that the elongations are in this case "falsely attributed to astigmatism" and he adds no brackets to "falsely."

Figs. 147a&b

Fig. 148

Fig. 149

And now we come to El Greco and to Ahlström who, so it seems, discovered a pattern of elongations and distortions in some paintings by El Greco. He believes these distortions to be astigmatic in nature — the meridian of strongest ocular refraction being about 15 degrees off the horizontal. This type of astigmatism is still counted as "against-the-rule" and will make us expect mainly vertical elongations in the artist's ocular images. There is *some* evidence in *some* of El Greco's paintings for this type of reoccurring "shape" distortion and for that, Ahlström might have a case. (I would rather repeat before going any further that the large, deliberate, mannerist distortions in the religious fantasy paintings have little to do with this ocular astigmatism.) Ahlström did point a finger at *some* details, *some* rather subtle mislocations in *some* of El Greco's portrait paintings and the repetitive character, the stability, the very subtleness of these distortions speak for some physical, optical, physiological (more precisely, ocular) cause. Ahlström's idea was that the cause was astigmatism. He also must have found out where to look for such optical distortions: not among the normal, schematized, commissioned portraits, not among those great (I also mean large) religious displays with all their disjointed extravaganzas — the distortions for which El Greco is famous and for which no ocular optical defect could account. Our author chose the Metropolitan Museum's portrait of the "Cardinal Grand Inquisitor" (see Fig. 20) with the eyeglasses, as the paradigm for his investigation of El Greco's assumed astigmatism. He could have hardly made a better choice. It is a great, almost overambitious piece done by a master portraitist in the manner which by that time must have become standardized mainly for the portraits of popes.* I usually refer to them as "armchair portraits." Raphael's Julius II (Fig. 148) and the portrait of Innocent X by Velázquez (Fig. 149) are some famous examples. Neither of these two artists could have had astigmatism. Every detail in these two portraits is in its correct place.

There is more to El Greco's Grand Inquisitor portrait (Figs. 150a & b). As I look at it with a change of attitude, I see that this portrait is indeed quite lopsided. I can now see that the floor is sagging toward the lower right. Note the subject's slippers — the left foot is lower! The should-be horizontal line — the molding in which floor and wall meet — is far from being horizontal. And that tale-telling top horizontal bar of the back of the armchair? It certainly does not run straight across as it does in the Raphael and the Velazquez portraits. It slopes toward the right lower edge of the canvas. The same is true for another "armchair portrait," also of a cleric — the full portrait of "Brother Paravicino" (Fig. 151) in the Boston Museum of Fine Arts and one of the great El Greco paintings. ("What a difference," I tell myself as I look once more at the Raphael and the Velázquez portraits. That bar of the back of the chair is a straight horizontal in both pictures.) But as we continue looking at the Grand Inquisitor there is even more to see. The arms and obviously the arm-supports are not on a level. Maybe the subject's left eye is also lower than the other eye. I notice also

*Several papal portraits show their subjects wearing a short, sleeveless tunic. The two cardinals portrayed by El Greco — our Grand Inquisitor and Cardinal Tavera — wear similar tunics. It must be a piece of vestment worn only by the highest church dignitaries.

that the whole figure seems shifted toward the left, as if the subject had been sitting on the edge of his chair (on the edge nearer to the left border of the canvas). Thus, too much of the back of the chair is visible on the other side. Such distortions, such misplacing could have quite reasonably been caused by a somewhat oblique but mainly "against-the-rule" astigmatism in El Greco's eye (note the singular!).

What is most convincing in the El Greco case is the repetitive nature of the distortion. We can find it in more than one instance — only in portraits not in the great fantasy displays — and the type of portraits in which we can find it have some common characteristics. Once the eye is alerted we will easily recognize the same or similar distortion details and also the particular type of subjects in which they might manifest themselves.

Another El Greco painting studied and photographed by Ahlström (Figs. 152a & b) is a double-portrait of Sts. Peter and Paul (which I have already mentioned in my short survey of visual aids). It was a rather poor choice — a not very important and not very convincing example. It belongs in a kind of transitional group: saints but human; portraits, but not in the word's strictest sense. The astigmatic distortion is not very noticeable and the "twin" photograph does not strike me as much improved. The twin portraits (Figs. 150a & b; Figs. 152a & b) offer a way to "normalize" the distorted portraits. Figures 150a and 152a are photographs of the originals, Figures 150b and 152b, taken with an inverted cylindrical telescope. This makes the portraits more "normal" and much less interesting.

Figs. 150a&b

Fig. 151

Looking with a "brain-washed" eye, I also discovered some other "real" portraits that could belong to Ahlström's astigmatic group. Two fine examples are the likenesses of Cardinal Tavera (Fig. 153) in Toledo and of Canon Covarrubias (Fig. 154) in Rumania. Doing these two portraits the artist still observed all the "Vermeer" rules: light from left, face turned toward the light, eyes turned toward painter, etc. But he did not or could not ignore anymore the play of light on mature faces molded by "the days of our years." He could not afford flattering with a flat brush (flat —flattery!). To produce a beautiful portrait of, say, the Cardinal Grand Inquisitor of Spain would be disrespectful — almost an offense. This clever Levantine knew the rules. Also, he could not ignore the vestments of high office. The repetitious frills around the neck would not do in these cases. He had to apply himself to details furnished by his actual retinal image rather than submit to the routine of his hand (or of his assistants' hands). And if astigmatism has any bearing upon portraiture then this is where a distorted optical image would obtrude upon the canvas. Looking thus, mentally prepared ("brain-washed" is such an excellent metaphor), we can now really see that (in the Canon's case) the left sleeve, the hands, and the open book, all pull toward the lower right corner. The details in that region are all somewhat oversized in comparison with a relatively small head. (Note, by the way, the divergence of the left eye with more of the inside white of this eye showing.) Another good example is an early portrait of St. Francis (Fig. 155). It looks quite naturalistic. It looks like a real portrait of somebody. The distortion in the down-and-to-the-right direction is clearly recognizable. (Note that the fingers are not short and stubby.)

Of great interest here are two almost identical paintings of St. Jerome — one in the National Gallery in London, and one in the Frick Collection (Fig. 156). These Jerome pictures are, except for the heads, copies of the portrait of the Cardinal Tavera. (Note the vestments, the hands, and the book.) El Greco did not mind copying himself once he found some successful arrangement of composition details. (Or maybe it was done by

Fig. 152a&b

Fig. 153

Fig. 154

his assisting students?) The main difference, in this instance, is seen in the heads — the way he handled hair and beard. Note the well-groomed, sparing elegance of the high cleric, and the imagination free of restraint when painting the imaginary portraits of the Saint. Here El Greco felt he could dispose of the constraints and the conventions of commissioned portraiture. He dared to paint asymmetric faces and diverging eyes. And he dared, more and more, to show in portraits of elderly people (in the particular type of portrait that did not have to be "beautiful") what his retinal images actually told him about them.

Let me return to Holbein's Henry VIII for a moment. It is, I think, the most convincing and easiest understood among Ahlström's choices. Holbein was an uncomplicated German-Swiss artisan-artist, endowed with a colossal talent. His paintings closely represent his actual retinal image.

Retinal images play a somewhat subordinate role in the perception of our world, even in the artist's world. The laws of constancy often overrule the laws of optics. Take "constancy of size" as an example. We do not see a person "smaller" when his image on our retina shrinks because of increasing distance between us and him. We have to be artists to see what the retinal image tells us. And then we can still take it or leave it. El Greco might not have noticed in the beginning that he inadvertently left more room for details in the lower right corner of his canvas. But he would have certainly noticed it, had he painted thick, ugly fingers on account of his astigmatism. He must have learned how to paint an acceptable hand whatever the orientation of the fingers. "Constancy" and "learning" replace, modify and complete the optical impression. Modigliani is an instructive example to look at. Pleasantly curved, "sexy" elongations along a cranio-caudal axis of symmetry are his marks of identity. Astigmatism "against-the-rule" might have quite well been a determinant factor in the evolution of his personal style. But it does not follow that a reclining nude by the same artist must be fat and short. Modigliani would have never painted reclining nudes short and fat just to fit his retinal image.

Fig. 155

Fig. 156

SUMMING IT ALL UP

In trying to "sum it all up" I find myself facing some difficulties. I faced similar difficulties when I tried to decide how to limit the scope of my observations: to limit them to just a few of the most conspicuous aspects of certain artworks.

What kind of artworks? What kind of artists? I tried to make choices primarily in terms of what to omit. For instance, I decided not to touch on one aspect: color — though I have contributed to the literature of the physiology and pathophysiology of color vision. The use of color by any artist is not pertinent for the ophthalmologist trained in deciphering possible visual-perceptual defects or peculiarities. For the same reason, my choice of artworks was based neither on beauty nor on artistic excellence. (Personal predilection, of course, might have played some role.)

There is a lingering question in the back of my mind: Is the appreciation of art enhanced — as some of my ex-students told me several years after having attended my lectures on art — if the viewer looks for and learns to recognize visual distortions? I am referring to distortions which are possibly due to the artist's visual defects rather than to a personal idiosyncratic manner, his unique personal style.

After considerable reflection in this matter I came to the conclusion that some (perhaps many) genuine art enthusiasts prefer knowledge to naive admiration, and their pleasure in viewing and studying art is enhanced rather than diminished by a scientific exploration of certain aspects of the creative process. This is the audience to whom I have addressed myself and with whom I wish to share my observations.